# The Outside Story

**VOLUME 2**

# The Outside Story

Writers explore the nature of the Northeast | **VOLUME 2**

Produced by

Northern Woodlands

Sponsored by grants from the Wellborn Ecology Fund of

NEW HAMPSHIRE
CHARITABLE FOUNDATION

Northern Woodlands
P.O. Box 471
1776 Center Road
Corinth, Vermont 05039
(802) 439-6292

For bulk sales or ordering information, call (802) 439-6292 or email mail@northernwoodlands.org

Printed in the United States of America by Sheridan Books
Project management by Patrick White, Northern Woodlands
Designed by Lisa Cadieux, Liquid Studio
Proofread by Marian Cawley
Index by Jennifer Spanier, Spanier Indexing
Cover painting and interior art by Adelaide Tyrol



Library of Congress Control Number 2016931552

ISBN 978-0-9786599-5-0

First printing, 2016

1 2 3 4 5 6 7 8 9 10 16 17 18 19 20

# Dedication

This collection of essays is dedicated to Marguerite Wellborn, writer, naturalist, and philanthropist, whose extraordinary generosity has touched the lives of thousands of people across New Hampshire and Vermont.

Marguerite Wellborn spent most of her childhood on a hill farm in the Mohawk River watershed of New York state, an environment short on playmates but rich in natural woodlands and wild and domestic animals. Here she learned to cherish the ecology of our planet. All her life, an ordinary walk in the woods was for her a voyage of miraculous discoveries.

Her personal bent was scholarly, so she not only spent time observing the daily activities of many species but also memorized taxonomies, studied what other scholars had discovered, and sent out this news via her succinct and elegant prose.

Her assumption that an education can illuminate human decisions, and her fear that human ignorance of biological systems will inevitably destroy them, motivated her to establish the Wellborn Ecology Fund. At an advanced age, when her personal energy was failing but her financial resources had greatly increased, she offered this gift to the residents of Vermont and New Hampshire with the hope that it would diminish ignorance and increase a sense of responsibility for the web of life that she once described as, "beautifully simple and awesomely complex."

She would have been delighted by this second book of inspiring essays on her favorite subject.

Sally Wellborn
June 24, 2016

# Contents

# Foreword

RICHARD OBER

## "If you don't know the ground, you are probably wrong about nearly everything else."

Norman Maclean's line from *Young Men and Fire* is silkscreened on my office wall, right above Philip Carrigain's iconic 1816 map of New Hampshire. During 20 years of working for land trusts and eight in community philanthropy, I have woven the line into speeches, the epigraph of a book, and countless conversations. It is in the DNA of the New Hampshire Charitable Foundation.

Because place matters.

That is the spirit of this remarkable collection and the woman who made it possible: Marguerite Wellborn. As Elise Tillinghast writes in her introduction, Marguerite understood that "knowing your place is a lifelong adventure." With the Wellborn Ecology Fund, she left a tremendous philanthropic legacy to guide the way to that adventure, and to knowledge and stewardship of this remarkable place for generations to come.

Her fund at the Foundation supports place-based ecology education in schools, professional development for teachers, farm-to-school initiatives – and *The Outside Story*.

Every week, *The Outside Story* essays unfold from the river valleys and hills, the soils and rocks, the birds and mammals, and insects and fish and microbes that comprise these communities, natural and human, that we call New Hampshire and Vermont – especially the Upper Valley. They quite literally could not have been written anywhere else. Because these writers – these talented and passionate and observant writers – are as much of these places as are the natural phenomena they explore.

In short, these authors know the ground. And in nature writing – as in land conservation and in community philanthropy – everything else starts there.

Richard Ober is president and CEO, New Hampshire Charitable Foundation.

# Preface

ELISE TILLINGHAST

If you stand in a patch of goldenrod, you may notice that some of the stalks have bulges that are roughly the shape and size of ping pong balls. These are galls, created by tiny grubs that, come spring, will pupate and emerge as small, short-lived flies.

Last winter, inspired by Barbara Mackay's activity page about goldenrod galls that's included in the appendix of this book, I organized a family expedition. We collected a bouquet of galls from a snowy field and retreated to the kitchen, where my husband and I used knives to pry them open.

Some came apart in a powdery mess. Some had been pierced all the way to the center by sharp-beaked birds. But in most of the galls we uncovered plump white larvae, perhaps a centimeter in length, tucked snugly inside woody cavities. My young son and daughter held the grubs in their hands, where they soon warmed up and began to squirm. We studied them under a microscope, and used a flashlight to illuminate exit holes hidden just beneath the galls' skin. Finally, we put the grubs back into their cradles, pieced the galls together as best we could with masking tape, and returned them to the field.

This was a great learning experience about an insect-plant relationship that I'd never really noticed before. It was also just plain fun. And although, yes, I realize that not everyone's perfect day involves handling fly larvae, I hope that as you thumb through this book you'll also have moments where a subject snags your interest, and prompts you to go outside and take a closer look.

This second volume of selections from *The Outside Story* series includes essays that were published between 2006 and 2015. It is truly a collaborative effort, representing the work of 39 different writers, as well as editors from *Northern Woodlands* magazine. Artist Adelaide Tyrol contributed the illustrations – as she has from the very beginning of the series, back in 2002. And of course there were many unsung heroes – scientists, wildlife experts, foresters, and other knowledgeable folks who gave their time, often on short notice, to make sure that what made it into print was accurate.

Although we've covered a lot of ground in this last decade, the series continues to focus, for the most part, on common species and natural phenomena that you can observe in the forests and fields around your home. You would think that, with 52 essays published every year, we'd eventually run out of topics, but so far that hasn't happened. Whether it's meat-eating trees, energy-maximizing chipmunks, or clams that lurk on the forest floor, local nature is an endlessly surprising and generous subject.

Marguerite Wellborn, whose remarkable bequest to the New Hampshire Charitable Foundation inspired *The Outside Story* series, believed that knowledge is the key to environmental preservation. As her own history as a naturalist and writer demonstrated, knowing your place is a lifelong adventure. There's so much to explore just outside our doors. All of it enriches our lives, and is worthy of our stewardship.

Elise Tillinghast is the executive director of the Center for Northern Woodlands Education, and publisher of *Northern Woodlands* magazine.

# Acknowledgments

We can't possibly thank everyone who contributed in some way to this book, but here is a list of main culprits:

Patrick White managed the publication of this book, with a lot of help and advice from Amy Peberdy. Lisa Cadieux of Liquid Studio is responsible for the design of this book, and thanks are due as well to Marian Cawley for her keen-eyed copyediting.

A number of editors had a hand in *The Outside Story* series during the period of 2006-2015. They include Virginia Barlow, Stephen Long, Dave Mance III, Anne Margolis, Meghan Oliver, Elise Tillinghast, Dirk Van Susteren, Patrick White, and Chuck Wooster.

Particular thanks to Virginia Barlow, whose collection of calendar entries opens each chapter.

Barbara Mackay wrote and personally tested the activities in the appendix of this book. Thank you, Barb! Also special thanks to Lisa Purcell of Four Winds Nature Institute, and Hannah Putnam of the Vermont Institute of Natural Science, for their early advice and encouragement.

Adelaide Tyrol is responsible for all of the artwork in this book, including the beautiful cover painting. You can learn more about her work at: adelaidetyrol.com.

Emily Rowe is responsible for the distribution and online promotion of the series, and responds to editors' last minute changes with serenity.

Finally, a special shout out to Kevin Peterson and Lois Shea of the New Hampshire Charitable Foundation for their support of this project, and to the foundation's Wellborn Ecology Fund, which has made both *The Outside Story* series, and this book, possible. Thank you.

# The Outside Story

**VOLUME 2**

# january

## first week

Night of Jan 3-4: The Quadrantids produce bright fireballs and can be the strongest shower of the year but, alas, clouds are common on January nights.

Coyotes begin mating.

Orion the Hunter is in the southern sky, best seen in January and February.

As cold weather settles in, grouse may form coveys and roost in the low branches of conifers, seeking protection from the wind.

## second week

Cedar waxwings are often in large flocks and can strip a crabapple of its fruits in short order.

Mated pairs of pileated woodpeckers stay together year-round, though they roost in separate tree cavities at night.

Wrapping the trunks of young, thin-barked yard trees with commercial tree wrap may help prevent sunscald. Remove it in the spring.

Downy woodpeckers are digging into tree trunks to find wood-boring beetle larvae, a favorite fat-rich winter food.

# third week

A turtle's metabolism slows almost to zero and these animals can survive in the mud at the bottom of streams where there is very little oxygen.

If the snow is not too deep, look for the fruiting stalks of ostrich fern. They're feather-shaped and the stalk has a deep groove. You might want to return in May to pick the edible fiddleheads.

Raccoons will be out and about during warm spells. They're dormant when it's cold but they don't really hibernate.

# fourth week

The "January thaw" used to be a bit more reliable than it is nowadays, but if there is one, it's likely to be ending about now.

The tufted titmouse isn't likely to be in a flock of its own species but will often join a chickadee flock.

Look for redpolls in the ragweed patch.

Cedar swamps provide cover and food for deer. Moose don't like cedar; for them it's starvation food.

Male dark-eyed juncos are wintering farther north than the smaller females.

# *Spishing* in the Woods

BRYAN PFEIFFER

When nature calls, a birdwatcher should consider *spishing* in the woods. Nature calling, in this case, is the unmusical peeps, chips, tweets, whits, and other "call notes" of songbirds in winter. Lacking the imperative to breed, even our most melodious songbirds rarely sing when the days are brief and cold. Instead, they issue short notes, mostly one- or two-syllable forms of communication.

If you'd like to see or hear more birds this time of year, issue some notes and noises of your own. A repeated, soft wispy "*spshsh-spshsh-spshsh*" is bird parlance for danger. A birder *spishing* is imitating the scolding or warning notes that some songbirds utter to alert others of a lurking predator. It's a universal alarm call. So when you spish, songbirds often pop into view to investigate.

Consider the encounter I had during a winter bird count on Long Island. While bush-whacking through scrubby oak-pine woodlands, the only bird note I heard was the thin high *tseep* of a white-throated sparrow. The woods were otherwise silent. Vacant. But I suspected otherwise. So I stopped and *spished.*

*"Spshsh-spshsh-spshsh-spshsh. Psssp-psssp-psssp-psssp-psssp. Spshsh-spshsh-spshsh-spshsh."*

Two white-throated sparrows jumped into view from a tangle of catbrier. Then several more. An eastern towhee belted out a plucky *reeEEP*! I kept *spishing.* A northern cardinal emerged and uttered its short, bright *peek* note. Two hermit thrushes popped onto a white oak branch, flicked their wings, and repeated a couple of soft *chuck* calls.

But the concert was only beginning.

I enhanced the ruse by adding the rolling whistle of an eastern screech owl. Soon the trees and brambles were alive with more birds: a red-bellied woodpecker, a half-dozen black-capped chickadees, several tufted titmouse, a winter wren, three more towhees, two brown thrashers, a gray catbird, a northern mockingbird, and a few yellow-rumped warblers.

The owl call, combined with *spishing*, really grabbed their attention. The reason? Owls hunt songbirds by stealth. In silent, deadly flight they surprise their prey, closing the deal with a well-practiced grasp of the talons. My whistled screech owl actually attracted the other birds, which were flying in to determine the location of the predator. A songbird that might otherwise become owl food can avoid danger if it knows where the owl is perched.

Your best ally in this ruse to attract songbirds is the black-capped chickadee. The chickadee is often the first species to respond to *spishing* or to the whistle of the screech owl. Chickadees will issue a high-intensity *zeeet* call in response to a rapidly approaching predator, such as a hawk or owl in flight, or a dog or human walking into their territory. They will deliver the more familiar *chick-a-dee-dee* alerts in the presence of a stationary predator. Researchers have concluded that chickadees vary the rate or urgency of this call or add more *dee* notes to convey the distance or immediacy of the threat.

Chickadees approach the scene of perceived danger because they recognize strength and safety in numbers. They respond to your *spishing* with their warning calls, but then a mob of them will gather and converge on a perched hawk or owl, scolding it with notes or even dive-bombing the raptor to harass it out of the territory. Other songbird species are likely to notice and join the fracas.

Incidentally, danger isn't the only thing that gets birds calling. They call out during feeding and courtship. Night-flying songbirds call to keep the flock together in the dark. Some birds that herd together during breeding, such as gulls and gannets, use call notes to help mates keep track of each other.

You can try all this on your own at home. Head outside into the snow, find a flock of black-capped chickadees and begin *spishing*. Be patient. It may take a few minutes to get the gang together. Approach slowly. Avoid sudden, jerky movement. The chickadee chatter will build, and soon a hairy woodpecker, white-breasted or red-breasted nuthatch, tufted titmouse, or even a golden-crowned kinglet may join the mob.

As with any bird-questing technique, excessive *spishing* can become a form of harassment, so don't overdo it – especially during the spring breeding season. Once the birds respond, lay off the *spishing* and enjoy the show.

Then invite the neighbors over to explain what you've been doing. You'll dispel rumors that you've lost your marbles and are hissing at trees.

# Blobs on Ice:
# Jelly Fungi Add Color to the Winter Landscape

JOE RANKIN

They look like blobs of shiny tar, a melted lollipop, or a crayon left in the sun too long. They come in vivid colors from orange to yellow to white to black to pinkish. They have a disconcerting ability to mimic human body parts, such as ears and tongues, with a Daliesque artfulness.

Jelly fungi.

They got their name because their tissues have the texture and consistency of, well, jelly. In some cases it's more like rubber. The various species often carry imaginative common names: witch's butter, snow fungus, jelly ear.

"They can often be very beautiful and very colorful, and the jelly-like mass represents the reproductive tissues that produce sexual spores," said Terrence Delaney, a biologist and mycologist who studies plant pathogens and teaches courses on fungi at the University of Vermont.

The fact that you can often find jelly fungi in the winter may give the false impression that they grow even in the coldest months. While there are so-called winter mushrooms that fruit late in the season, the frozen, colorful blobs that you see aren't likely to be growing, explained Delaney. Rather, they're remnants of jelly fungi that last formed in the cool, damp days of autumn, then froze in a cold snap. The organisms that created them, however, are very much alive. They survive the winter under the wood or other substrate on which the jelly clings.

The colorful gelatinous growths that you see in the early spring are likely new growth, nourished by snowmelt and spring rains.

Despite appearances, the large group of jelly fungi are not a single family of closely related species. "They're a tremendously diverse group," said Delaney. "You'd be surprised at how two similar-appearing jelly fungi can be only distantly related. For example, two orange jelly fungi may be less closely related than are humans to hummingbirds." The similar, gelatinous bodies of jelly fungi are an example of convergent evolution, where different organisms evolve independently and come to the same solution to a problem – in this case, to manage the vagaries of hydration and desiccation.

A jelly fungus' microscopic sexual cells, called basidia, reveal more evidence of the differences within the group. In some, the cells are "Y-shaped," like a tuning fork, while in others they are round but divided into chambers, like an orange with four wedges. These features, and consideration of whether their substrate is decaying hardwood or softwood, can help you identify different species of jelly fungi.

For scientists, jelly fungi pose some research challenges. For one thing, there's getting the specimen home in decent shape. Another is preserving it. To identify a species and place it within a group of fungi is especially challenging during dry times of the year, when jelly fungi are nothing more than dry, scale-like stuff on logs or dying trees. But when it rains, their gelatin-like matrix absorbs moisture like a sponge. It's an adaptation that allows the fungi to take almost instant advantage of wet spells. Rather than having to "build" new spore-producing components from scratch, like most cap mushrooms, jelly fungi just have to rehydrate their bodies.

Another interesting thing about jelly fungi: while many of them feed on decaying wood, some eat other fungi, a not uncommon occurrence among the mushroom clan. The Collybia jelly, *Syzgospora mycetophila*, for instance, preys on the common *Gymnopus dryophilus* mushroom. Witch's butter, *Tremella mesenterica*, also known as golden brain, yellow trembler, and golden jelly fungus, is a parasite on the mycelium of a wood-decay fungus.

When it comes to getting eaten by humans, the jelly fungi don't have much to worry about. Many species are edible, but most just don't taste like anything and have an unpleasant rubbery texture. The apricot jelly is a tongue-shaped fungus that's sometimes harvested and sold. George Barron, in his field guide *Mushrooms of Northeast North America*, noted that the distinctive apricot coloring really dresses up a mixed salad, but doesn't contribute any taste.

While they're not going to help feed the world, jelly fungi will continue to play their part in breaking down organic matter, and that's no small thing.

# Catch a Falling Snowflake

Barbara Mackay

Who hasn't marveled at a lacy snowflake coming to rest on a jacket sleeve? Do you wonder how it could survive the fall to earth in one piece, or if it's really true that no two snowflakes can look exactly alike?

A snowflake begins high up in the clouds, not as a snowflake but as a small particle of dust, salt, or ash. When a cloud cools below 32 degrees, some specks of water vapor freeze onto the particle. As it moves through the cloud, the particle absorbs additional water vapor, building up microscopic layers of ice. When water molecules freeze, they bond together in a way that forms a six-sided ice crystal.

Eventually, the ice crystal becomes too heavy to stay aloft in the cloud, and it begins the descent to earth, usually with many others like itself. This is the precipitation we call snow. A snowflake can be a single ice crystal, but it's usually a cluster of crystals, often 200 or more, all symmetrically connected. The common feature of all ice crystals, and thus all snowflakes, is the hexagonal structure of branches, short stub-like arms, or sides.

Snow crystals are categorized by their general shape. There is the familiar intricate star-shaped snowflake, called a stellar dendrite. Spatial dendrites also have branches, but they are more untidy and dissimilar. Plates have just the suggestion of arms growing at the six corners of the hexagon. Other common types are needles, columns (which look like short, unsharpened pencils), and capped columns (which look like columns with graduation caps attached to the ends). Eighty snow crystal varieties have been formally identified, catalogued, and labelled by scientists who study the world of winter. Two books with exquisite photographs are *The Snowflake: Winter's Secret Beauty* (Libbrecht and Rasmussen) and *Snow Crystals* (Bentley and Humphreys).

Different cloud temperatures and humidity levels determine the snow crystal's initial size and shape. Thin, plate-like crystals grow when temperatures are close to the freezing point. At cooler temperatures, needles, columns, and dendrites appear. Additionally, higher humidity produces more intricate designs, while simpler forms of plates and columns occur in drier air.

Finding a perfectly intact snowflake is a treat. In a 30-minute free-fall, snow crystals are tossed about by the wind, encounter different temperatures and levels of humidity, and get in each other's way. Pieces may break off or melt, or crystals that collide might stick together. So, can two snowflakes be exactly alike? Only if they attract water vapor in a cloud in exactly the same way, fall through exactly the same temperature and moisture conditions, and swirl in identical aerial dances. Perhaps a statistician could give the odds, but I rather enjoy conducting my own research during a snowstorm.

It is easy to collect snowflakes for your own enjoyment and study. Keep a sheet of stiff black paper in the freezer, ready to grab when flakes start falling. Stand out of the wind and let snowflakes land on the paper. Then retreat to a protected area that is cold, such as a garage or covered deck. Use a magnifying glass to study the individual flakes. The hardest part is not breathing warm air on them!

You can also preserve snowflakes on a glass microscope slide. Keep the slide in the freezer and a can of clear acrylic spray in the refrigerator. When you are ready to go outside, put on gloves (you do not want the slide to warm up in your hands), spray the acrylic onto the slide, and dash outside. You can hold the slide in your outstretched hand, or place it on a level spot. Let a few flakes fall onto it, then place it in a protected spot outside for a few hours. The snowflakes will freeze into the plastic spray, which also freezes, creating a permanent impression of your snowflakes. Under the microscope you will be able to see tiny parts of snowflakes that you missed with your own eyes.

For a fun winter activity related to this essay, turn to page 218.

# Snowshoe Hares in Winter

CELIA EVANS

For the past 14 years, students in my winter ecology class and I have spent a lot of time outdoors, studying the preferred habitat features and winter foods of snowshoe hares. We're likely to find hare tracks hopping in and around lowland conifers near wetland edges, and then again at higher elevations, where the forest transitions into fir, birch, and spruce. Where we won't find them, at least not very often, is in broad bands of open, leafless hardwood. On the rare occasions that we find tracks in this habitat, they have almost always been single strands of widely spaced prints – suggesting an animal that's really moving!

The highest densities of hares tend to be in regenerating conifer stands where the fir and spruce trees are tall enough to provide protection from owls and other avian predators, but still dense enough to offer lots of horizontal protection from terrestrial carnivores like coyotes. When hares aren't feeding, they hunker down in depressions, called "forms." These are typically protected by low-hanging branches that are weighted down with snow, or under a mess of woody debris.

Protection is crucial to hares, for despite their white winter coats and those famous hind feet that facilitate fast getaways across the snow, they are constantly at risk of being eaten. Adult survival rates are rarely more than 30 percent, even in ideal habitat, and an estimated 80 percent of hares die from predation. A three-year-old hare is both old and lucky.

So what do snowshoe hares eat in their protected hiding places? In winter, they subsist mostly on small twigs, about one-tenth to one-fifth of an inch in width. My students have repeatedly counted all the twigs in sampling areas that have been browsed by hares, as well as all the twigs that were left alone. What we've found is that, while hares mostly avoid the branches of conifers (no surprise – imagine licking a pitch pocket of balsam fir), they didn't seem to have a preference among the shade-tolerant hardwood species that grew in our study area. They tended to eat these species – striped maple, red maple, American beech, wild raisin, and alder – in proportion to their availability.

We also tested hares' taste for wood species that didn't appear in our study area, including poplars and birch. Our experiments showed that the hares consistently preferred these hard-to-find twigs. As to why they had this preference, there's no clear answer – there's been extensive research on hare food preferences, but it points in different directions. A lack of chemical deterrents or the availability of particular nutrients, soluble carbohydrates, and perhaps sodium content may have been factors.

What we do know is that hares have an ingenious (if to many humans, repellent) way of making the most out of their meals: they digest them twice. Snowshoe hares, along with other hares and rabbits, have a small sac behind the intestines called a caecum. In this sac, there is a community of microorganisms that can break down the cellulose (the carbon compound that makes up most of wood). The only problem with this process, called hind-gut fermentation, is that it occurs after the food has passed the area where absorption takes place. To get around this, hares practice coprophagy – they defecate and then eat the soft pellets. Hares have a separate compartment in their stomachs where these re-ingested pellets ferment a little longer before passing through the intestines where the nutrients are absorbed.

So, if you're out in a patch of conifers this winter, keep a look out for signs of snowshoe hares. Their tracks are distinctive – often, the impressions of their big hind feet appear just ahead of the impressions of their front feet – this is caused by their bounding motion. You may also find slightly flattened, fibrous brown pellets and signs of browsing – look for slender twigs neatly snipped at 45-degree angles.

# In Search of the Pre-Settlement Forest

STEPHEN LONG

If you wanted to learn what the local forest was like before Europeans arrived in the eighteenth century, what would you do? One obvious approach would be to visit the few remaining bits of old growth forests in the region and draw your conclusions from what you see there today. Those remnant forests, however, would give you a picture that wouldn't be particularly accurate, according to plant ecologist Charlie Cogbill.

"We have patches that have survived for a long time, but almost to the one, they survived for very straightforward but significant reasons: they weren't logged, they weren't sought for clearance of land, they weren't agricultural, they couldn't be gotten to. The remnant stands are the oddballs, they are the extremes," said Cogbill.

Rather than the oddball, Cogbill has spent a large part of his career studying the typical pre-settlement forest. Piecing together a forest that no longer exists is the work of a detective, and Cogbill's detective work began in the 1970s while he was completing a master's degree at Hubbard Brook Experimental Forest in Woodstock, New Hampshire, studying forest dynamics. As he tried to better understand the ways in which human activity has changed our forests, he began his archival search for baseline information on the forest that was here before it was cleared for agriculture.

The documents that have proved most revealing to Cogbill are "lotting" surveys, the surveys by which the proprietors of a new town divided the town into lots for the earliest settlers. At each lot corner, the surveyors tended to place a monument, often a post or stake or a pile of stones. They also routinely made mention of a nearby "witness tree."

Cogbill compiles data on every tree mentioned in the surveys and then calculates the relative abundance of the tree species in each town. Fighting through naming nuances and regionalisms – for instance, black gum is called pepperidge in Connecticut, swampwood in Massachusetts, beetle wood in Vermont, and wild pear in New Hampshire – he has been able to paint a detailed and localized picture of what the forests of Vermont and New Hampshire looked like centuries ago.

That forest was quite different from today's. "There's been a monumental shift in the amount of beech from pre-settlement days, when there was a huge amount of beech everywhere. In northern New England, it was 40 percent of the original forest throughout almost the entire area. Today, according to FIA (forest inventory and analysis, compiled by the U.S. Forest Service) figures, it's more like 15 percent," Cogbill said.

Whether one specific area of beech was replaced by maple forest is not so easily seen, but the overall shift is clear, and the loss of beech is not a result of beech bark disease, which began in the last century, long after its population decline had begun.

Spruce is another species that was once more common. "Spruce has declined significantly, not just in the spruce zone of the high mountains but in the mixed woods on the uplands," said Cogbill. "It was a major representative in the mixed woods in southwest New Hampshire and the Piedmont of Vermont, but coming out of the 1800s, spruce was removed as a player from the mixed forest. The forest we now see at Hubbard Brook, which was mostly spruce mixed with northern hardwoods, is now northern hardwoods. It's gone from our minds that that used to be where spruce was. That's not acid deposition. That happened before acid deposition. That was land use." Cogbill cited work by a U.S. Forest Service silviculturist named Westveld, who showed that when spruce was logged out of the mixed woods, it didn't come back.

Surprisingly, white pine's reversal has been in the other direction, toward plenty. "Pine is a tree that has a huge reputation for being abundant, but it simply wasn't a major tree on the uplands in northern New England. It shows up less than one percent regionally. It was very uncommon," said Cogbill. "There were areas along the rivers that had very merchantable pine that was harvested early on. Otherwise, in the uplands, they didn't have very much, or had a scattered tree here or there. The witness tree surveys show that pine was very localized in the major southern valleys."

Knowing what species made up the pre-settlement forest, however, doesn't suggest to Cogbill that we should be trying to re-create that forest. "That's unreachable. We really have gone through a bottleneck of land use, and it's not just recently. The major blow in northern New England was the original land clearance. We changed the soils, almost permanently. They're still productive, they're still soil, they haven't been paved over, but the natural progression has been disrupted. We're on a trajectory, and you can't force it back."

# How Birds of a Feather Survive Cold Weather

Michael J. Caduto

Two winters past, a pair of Carolina wrens frequented our bird feeder. The male greeted the dawn with an ebullient "tea-kettle, tea-kettle, tea-kettle." After sunset, the intrepid wrens retired to the warmth and safety of our barn. Early each day, when I opened the door, I bid them, "Good morning," and was reminded of a friend who once had an eastern towhee, another bird not common to the season, over-winter in his barn in Barnard, Vermont. The resourceful towhee roosted in the warm corner of the barn near the animals and helped itself to some of their grain.

Barns aside, visiting friends who enjoy the winter birds at our feeder often ask how any bird could possibly survive sub-zero nights. Answer: The shelter and insulation provided by thick evergreens and dense shrubs, which are the most common nocturnal winter roosts for many birds. One of our popular bird feeders hangs near a row of bushy white pines. Come sunset, blue jays, juncos, mourning doves, and cardinals fly into these pines and settle for the night, somewhat protected from cold winds, snow, and rain.

Birds also spend winter nights in hollow trees, in old nest cavities, under peeling bark, in vines covering buildings, and under eaves. Purple finches roost en masse in the pines and hemlocks. Birds that nest in cavities during breeding season often use tree hollows for winter shelter; these include chickadees, titmice, nuthatches, screech owls, and both downy and hairy woodpeckers. Wintering white-breasted nuthatches pool their body heat by huddling in groups of up to two dozen.

Turkeys and crows often flock in evergreen treetops, pooling body heat, the latter congregating in groups of as many as several hundred. Crows return to the same roost each night from as far as 20 miles away.

Not all birds take to the trees for protection. The ruffed grouse, for example, digs under snow or dive-bombs into a snow bank to hollow out a tunnel. Within this warmer snow shelter, in ideal circumstances, grouse will expend roughly half the energy they would need in the open. Grouse also have downy plumes that branch from their main feathers, a nice coat to wear while surrounded by snow.

With less daylight in winter, birds have less time to forage, just at the time of the year when they need more food for more energy to stay warm during the long night. The Carolina wrens that frequented our yard found the perfect combination: plentiful food and a shelter with an actual roof over their heads to help conserve energy.

In his book *Life in the Cold*, the renowned field biologist and winter ecologist Peter Marchand says that most songbirds have just enough fat reserves to survive one extremely cold winter night. So, it is critical that they retain their body heat as much as possible. To keep their body temperatures within the necessary range of 104 to 109 degrees, birds grow a thicker coat of insulating feathers as winter approaches. The winter coats of goldfinches and redpolls, for example, are 50 percent thicker than their summer plumage. Birds can also increase insulation by 50 percent, simply by fluffing up their feathers.

In extreme cold, birds tend to tuck in their necks, legs, and wings to avoid losing heat from these extremities. Scientists have found that reducing their exposed surface area by one-fourth decreases heat loss by an equal amount.

These and other heat-conservation techniques usually work, but when they prove inadequate, birds have yet another strategy at their disposal: shivering. When their body temperatures begin dropping, they shiver to generate body heat. According to Marchand, shivering goldfinches were observed increasing their typical heat output five-fold when exposed to very cold temperatures in a laboratory.

Besides shivering, birds have an internal heat exchange system that helps maintain their core temperature. As warm arterial blood is pumped toward the cold feet, that blood comes into close contact with the cooler blood returning through the veins to the heart. This near-contact warms the venal blood so that it doesn't unduly chill the body core as it returns to the heart.

As well-equipped as birds are for surviving winter nights, there are ways humans can help. Among them: create sheltering brush piles in the woods; leave dead trees standing for the birds that roost in cavities; cut small access holes in sheds for winter birds seeking shelter. Come spring, consider planting thick evergreens for winter cover and put in a few berry-bearing shrubs to provide cold-weather food.

And, finally, don't forget to leave that barn door open by just a feather for the wrens and towhees.

# february

# 1 first week

Well-fed red squirrels store apples or mushrooms in tree crotches.

The record moose antler spread is 81 inches and these huge structures are now dropping to the ground.

In the depths of winter, the temperature in a beaver lodge may average 60 degrees warmer than outdoors.

The carcasses of winter-killed deer are important food for bobcat, coyote, and fisher.

Barred owls lay their eggs in mid winter and incubate eggs and brood chicks through many blizzards.

# second week 2

The saw-whet owl makes a big noise for a small bird. Its monotonous toot-toot-toot, repeated endlessly, can be heard from far away.

A fox walks a straight line, one foot ahead of the other; so does a bobcat, but his prints are larger and slightly offset.

Cattail flower heads disintegrate throughout the winter, releasing their 125,000 or so seeds.

A dead or half-eaten mouse or small bird impaled on a hawthorn is probably the work of a northern shrike.

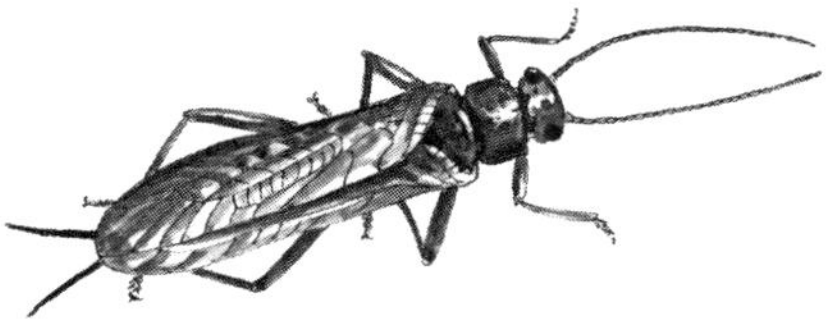





# third week

Chickadees have been fee-bee-ing for a while, but now they're ramping up the frequency and intensity of this territorial whistle.

The earliest stoneflies begin hatching. Fishermen prefer the later-hatching ones, from mid-March to late-April, when trout are becoming active.

At seven weeks old, black bear cubs now weigh about four pounds.

Like beaver lodges, the winter homes of muskrats have underwater entrances and they, too, may be stuck beneath the ice.

# fourth week

The mournful coo of the mourning dove has been mercifully absent all winter; you will hear it soon.

An owl's flight noise is about 1 KHz; mice can't hear much below 3 KHz and so don't hear the owl coming.

It's time to clean out birdhouses, except those being used by flying squirrels.

Bald eagles are checking out open water, hoping to see ducks.

Keep an eye out for pussy willows.
The opening flower buds are a sign that winter is losing its grip.

# Awkward Adolescent Eagles

Elise Tillinghast

A deer died by the river near my home. The crows found it, as did other scavengers – a bald eagle, and two big brown raptors that were hard to identify. Both had white flecking on their heads, wings, and bodies, but the markings didn't match up, bird to bird. They looked unkempt and more than a little disreputable.

It turns out these were also bald eagles, but young birds, dressed in dark plumage. In common with some other long-lived species, eagles have an extended adolescence. They require about four to five years to mature. During this period they don't find mates, establish territories, or conform to the adult dress code.

"They can really look a mess," said Chris Martin, a senior raptor biologist at New Hampshire Audubon. At the time an eagle fledges, its primary and secondary wing feathers – the big feathers along the back edge of the wing – are longer than they'll ever be again. This extra length makes the wing area greater and likely provides more lift for rookie flyers, although it lessens aerial grace.

As the fledgling wing feathers molt, beginning when the eagle is around nine months old, they grow back at the slightly shorter, adult length. The result is a jagged appearance that persists for about two years, until all of the original sets of primary and secondary feathers have been replaced. (Eye and beak color also change during adolescence; they start off dark and slowly transition to yellow.)

Although immature plumage is mostly brown, it's highly variable among individuals, which explains my birds' haphazard white markings. According to Todd Katzner, a wildlife biologist at the U.S. Geological Survey, there's some thought that this dark color has a signaling purpose. It may tell adult birds that youngsters aren't fully mature and thus not a threat to a breeding territory. What is certain, he said, is that in nesting season, when mated eagles are intolerant of adult eagle intruders, they're much more likely to let young birds linger nearby.

This tolerance is helpful because, unlike adults, immature eagles often travel hundreds of miles during nesting season, which begins in early spring and extends through summer. “They bounce around a lot,” said Martin.

So what are these youngsters doing, other than flying around and looking messy? “They’re experimenting,” Martin explained. “They’re learning how to make it in the world.” One of the ways they do this is by tailing mature eagles. From these elders, they learn where fish are concentrated, where to scavenge, what roosts offer the best thermal cover on cold nights.

They also play house. Katzner described how an immature eagle may join up with a bird of the opposite gender to practice building a nest. Often these nests will be “pretty shoddy,” he said, “but they learn to do better next time.”

Another critical aspect of a young eagle’s education is learning how to get along with others. While all eagle species are social, said Katzner, bald eagles take it to an extreme. They roost and forage in groups, and this means that they also get into more conflicts. “They’re sort of like humans that way.”

At a food site, or when crossing another bird’s territory, an immature eagle has to figure out how to assert itself, and how to back down from a fight. Typical of many bird species, “eagles do a lot of posturing, a lot of wing spreading and showing their talons,” explained Katzner. Learning this language is important to avoid getting wounded or even killed, and it can be a hard-won skill. “Some of them never learn,” said Martin.

They must also master the diplomatic art of circling. If you have ever noticed a pair of eagles performing what looks like a series of lazy rotations across the sky, what you may have witnessed was one eagle chasing the other away. Katzner calls this behavior “escorting a bird out of your territory,” and it’s a common way that mature eagles rid themselves of younger birds. If the escortee doesn’t understand the cue, or perhaps is a four-year-old bird that is feeling its hormones, then this circling can escalate into full out combat. In some cases, these fights result in interlocked talons and two giant raptors falling out of the sky. (Yes, this really happens.)

All told, learning to be an eagle is hard work. So the next time you see a scruffy brown raptor lurking among the crows, go easy on the kid. Don’t mock his messy coiffure. He’s still growing up, and has a lot on his mind.

# Shed Hunting

KUBIE BROWN



Whether we see them slinking silently through the shadows of a quiet forest, darting across the road, or standing alone in a yellowed field, the sight of a whitetail buck touches some ancient and primal part of our souls. In fall, a buck's antlers, rising and curling gracefully above his head, are impossible to miss. In spring, as the antlers lie waiting to be decomposed on the forest floor, they're almost impossible to find, though this doesn't keep shed hunters – both human and animal – from looking.

Whether you're a hunter looking to see if the buck that got away survived the winter, or a nature enthusiast looking to bring a part of the world you love home, antler shed hunting is gaining more and more popularity. It is a difficult and sometimes frustrating venture, but one that has many rewards for those who enjoy spending time in the woods.

Before we get to the finer points of shed hunting, we should review the antler. Unlike the "horns" that animals like cows and goats sport year-round, antlers grow from scratch and are discarded each year. Deer and moose begin growing their antlers in March or April, and they're fully grown by late August. When the antlers are growing, they are covered in a velvet-like material that supplies blood to the growing antlers. Prior to the breeding season, shortening day length causes a rise in a buck's testosterone levels, which directly relates to the hardening of the antler and the shedding of velvet. A buck will scrape off the velvet and polish the antlers in preparation for breeding season, during which time he may use them in a dominance fight with another buck. When the breeding season ends, usually late December in the Northeast, the buck no longer has any need for his antlers, and shortly thereafter the antler, devoid of any blood flow for several months, drops off, leaving a small bloody stump that quickly scabs over.

Finding shed antlers is an exercise in patience. It takes a lot of luck and hours of roaming the woodlands that bucks inhabit. The season for shed hunting begins in February – when most bucks around the Northeast lose their antlers – and continues through April. Shed hunters have to figure out where the bucks have been resting and feeding, and find the paths that they travel on. During the early season, especially in far northern areas, finding buck tracks in the snow and simply following them is very effective. Heavy snow will concentrate deer and the antlers they shed. Do be conscious, though, of animal stress, and avoid disturbing deeryards – the dense, evergreen forest stands in which they congregate. Instead, backtrack the animals from their core yards toward adjacent hardwood feeding areas, and look for shed antlers there.

In southern areas of Vermont and New Hampshire where deer don't, as a general rule, yard in winter, it's harder, but not impossible, to find sheds. Concentrate your search by eliminating areas where a buck is not likely to lose them. The middle of a field is a rare spot to find antlers, but areas of thickets and woods with heavily traveled deer trails are good places to look, as the thicker cover can simply tug the antlers off the buck's head. Fence crossings, fallen logs, and any such areas where a buck would have to leap over to cross are often worth an extra glance, as the impact of landing can jar the antlers to the ground. Both moose and deer are drawn to pathways. If you cannot locate any active deer trails, simply follow and search snowmobile trails and power lines that are naturally easy travel routes for these animals. The truth is that there is no definite formula to finding shed antlers; dropping off of bucks' heads at random times and places, the only sure way to find them is to get out and look.

March and early April are great times to find shed antlers; on good days the antlers will glow on the barren forest floor. But be aware that you're not the only one looking for sheds. Squirrels, mice, and porcupines, even foxes and bears, eat antlers, which are full of calcium, phosphorus, and mineral salts. By summer, wild animals large and small will have nearly devoured every antler in the forest.

# Buds: Spanning the Seasons

Michael Wojtech

The sign in the window, which read, "Clearance! Hats and Gloves 50% Off," puzzled me. Snowflakes swirled on gusty winds. The bitter cold stung my fingertips – I wondered if I should buy warmer gloves while I had the chance. Clearance? Temperatures hadn't climbed above freezing for days; the warmth of spring was a distant dream.

Blow out your boots, or lose your wool hat in winter, and when you go looking for a replacement you are likely to find sandals and sun hats on display. I used to rail against such a setup, assigning it to an insatiable human propensity for speed, afraid that at some point we might just lap ourselves. But when I began to study trees, and learned how their growth patterns transcend traditional seasonal boundaries, I softened my stance.

I began one summer by studying leaves – long and pointed, with coarsely toothed edges, on American beech; seven or so leaflets supported by a central stalk on white ash; the finely toothed leaves of paper birch. When autumn arrived, the leaves flashed brilliantly and fell, but the show wasn't over. The seemingly bare branches displayed buds for the next year's leaves and flowers that were, as botanist and writer Rutherford Platt described, "varied as jewelry, in all sorts of exquisite shapes and bright colors."

On beeches, the lance-like buds were such a vibrant chestnut-brown that I wondered how I could have previously overlooked them. The brown, pointed buds of paper birches were less prominent, but no less beautiful. The rounded buds on the tips of white ash twigs reminded me of the dome on a telescope observatory.

Through buds I continued studying leaves, without waiting for spring. I discovered that inside each bud miniature leaves grow into intricate ptyxes, or folding patterns. Multiple leaves and stems are packed together to allow the greatest volume in the smallest space, a process referred to as vernation, and one that reminds me of a hiker trying to fit weeks' worth of gear into a backpack.

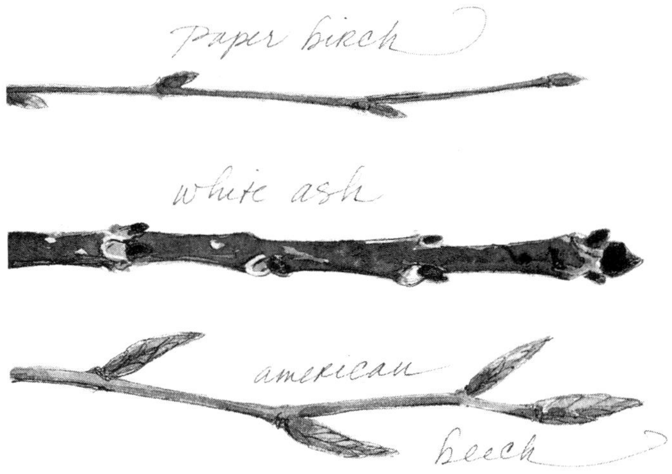

These folding patterns are so specific and varied that they warrant their own set of botanical terms. Beech leaves, for example, grow in a plicate pattern – pleated along the central rib. One theory holds that the unique leaf shape of each tree is derived, at least in part, from the need for efficient folding patterns within the bud.

Throughout winter and early spring I watched the buds swell and grow longer until they seemed ready to burst open, like racehorses at a starting gate. Buds, however, don't just open in response to a vagrant, unseasonably warm day or early season rain. Specific criteria – exposure to cold temperatures for a cumulative, but not necessarily continuous, period of time, followed by adequate day length and an accumulation of warm weather – must be met before buds break dormancy. Species, location on the tree, genetic variation, and the weather of the previous season influence the requirements of each bud.

The buds opened like slow-motion jack-in-the-boxes. Stems elongated. Miniature leaves unfolded and grew larger. The volume that grew from each tiny bud astounded me. For many species in our region, including American beech and white ash, an entire year's new leaves and new stems often originate from this single flourish, a process called determinate growth. These trees immediately develop new buds – at first smaller than the head of a pin – that will open in subsequent years. Other species, such as paper birch, have indeterminate growth – a series of buds form and open during the growing season before the following year's buds are produced.

With either growth form, the next year's buds, which are completed before the leaves fall in autumn, carry the legacy of seasons past. In spring, the number of leaves and the length of the shoots produced by each bud are greatly influenced by the previous summer's environmental conditions, such as temperature and moisture level.

The growth process of buds and leaves is a continuous cycle that blurs traditional seasonal boundaries. Planning ahead, it seems, has its advantages. This winter there is still time to find jeweled harbingers of spring along the branches. And if you just can't wait, cut some twigs at the end of February and place them in a vase in a sunny window. You'll get an early taste of spring.

For a fun winter activity related to essay, turn to page 220.

# Snow Fleas: Now You See Them, Now You Don't

Bill Amos

The other day, I noticed snow fleas dusting new snow around a maple trunk. These minuscule creatures – broadly known as springtails – are out in force, and I didn't hear them coming. Not that I could. But I like to imagine the thunder of millions of tiny footfalls as they migrate upwards from the snow cover, pushing and jostling as they climb. Just a short while ago, they were scattered below, on the ground, quietly eating organic tidbits.

Six thousand species of springtail populate the world, and the snow fleas we see in New Hampshire and Vermont are but one variety. They have cousins living afar in leaf litter, tree canopies, and on rocky shores. They can be found in dark caves and in sunny meadows, and on ice in Antarctica and warm lava on a Pacific island. They are practically everywhere. They have been around a long time, too, but have changed little over the ages. Fossils reveal that springtails existed 400 million years ago.

Snow fleas are elusive but staggeringly populous. More than 100,000 of them can live comfortably in one square meter of soil. Here in northern New England, it's their sudden emergence that catches our attention.

Sometimes so many snow fleas appear that the snow seems carpeted with ashes. Approach them, and the entire mass rises in a dark cloud, swirling chaotically before descending to coat the surface again. When there are fewer snow fleas, you might see only tiny black dots that suddenly vanish in your presence.

The scene can be so strange that you might think you're hallucinating.

Catch one if you can, and check it out. Under strong magnification, you will see a lumpy and segmented body with bluish reflective scales. The snow flea, only one-sixteenth of an inch long, lacks wings, but it has three pairs of legs. It also has two antennae and two clusters of eyes, 16 in each.

Turn the snow flea over and you will see something really unusual. Beneath its abdomen is one of the most extraordinary devices found in the animal world: a lever-like appendage held under tension by a two-hook clasp. It's this appendage that gives the snow flea its incredible jumping ability.

To understand how it works, think of a common spring-loaded mousetrap. Touch the trigger holding the peanut butter, and the wire bar slams shut. Now gently place the cocked mousetrap upside down on the floor. Tap it with a pencil, and the trap snaps and springs into the air. Finally, imagine tens of thousands of mousetraps flying in the air. That approximates what happens when you approach a bunch of snow fleas.

Undisturbed, the snow flea walks on snow or ground pleasantly feeding and going about its business. When you arrive, it leaps hundreds of times its own body length (think of a human jumping over the Empire State Building), followed by just about every other snow flea in the area.

Your arrival was just detected by a snow flea's eyes or antennae, and a nerve impulse was sent to the clasp, which instantly released the appendage that catapulted the little creature out of danger.

After landing, the clasp will quickly grab and hold the appendage while internal (hydrostatic) fluid pressure builds up until the lever again becomes a cocked spring.

The spring-like mechanism is not the only unusual feature on the underside of a snow flea. The tiny creature has a tubular peg used for "drinking" and taking in oxygen. Rapid absorption of moisture is necessary to rebuild that hydrostatic pressure in the lever.

For much of the year, it's a relatively uneventful scene down at ground level. Like other springtails, snow fleas spend most of their time feeding on soil bacteria, fungi, algae, pollen, and organic material. Sometimes, they devour microscopic animals like rotifers and nematode roundworms. (During their brief appearances on snow, they mostly eat pollen and algal cells that have settled out of the air.)

In spring, like many creatures, they mate. The reproductive process isn't dramatic: males and females are seemingly oblivious of each other. Males deposit stalked droplets of sperm on the ground, and a wandering female picks up a droplet by chance and whisks it into her genital opening. Fertilization occurs, and eggs are laid in the soil.

In a matter of days, tiny nymphs appear as simpler, smaller versions of the adults, and they begin their generally unnoticed lives – until winter, when they impress a human visitor with their circus acts in the snow.

# Live Weird, Die Young: The Virginia Opossum

Kenrick Vezina

On our back porch, in a pocket of light from the window, was what looked to be an oversized rat wearing white face powder. As it gobbled down cat food, it flashed a demented crocodile grin. My mother shrieked.

This was my first encounter with a Virginia opossum.

This species, still described as "neotropical" by some sources, has been moving north since at least the 1950s. In many parts of the Northeast, opossums (frequently shortened to "possums") are as familiar as squirrels. Yet this is no mere rodent.

Possums are the only marsupials native to North America. Despite appearances, they are closer kin to wombats and kangaroos than rats or Kiss bassist Gene Simmons. Marsupials branched off of the main mammalian family tree long ago, and many of the traits they exhibit offer a window into what ancient mammals were like. Many of these differences relate to reproduction. All marsupials have pouches. They need these because they are not, like most mammals, placental. Their young spend barely any time developing in the mother's body. They're born in a near-fetal state, and the tiny, naked, and blind young must make a scramble to the pouch where they can complete their development in relative safety.

Newborn possums are born only the size of honeybees, and many don't survive the trip to their mother's pouch. Those that do must locate one of 13 nipples, arrayed in a circle with one in the middle. As soon as a baby possum starts to suckle, the nipple swells in its mouth, effectively trapping it in place until it has grown big enough to free itself. Once out of the pouch, the baby possum, along with its littermates, will hitch a ride by clinging to its mother's back.

Females can have as few as four or as many as twenty-five offspring at a time, of which about eight make it to the pouch. It only takes the young ten months to reach sexual maturity, and in warmer climates with longer summers, possums can have up to three litters per year.

Easily the possum's most significant contribution to popular culture is the phrase "playing possum" – but when it comes to feigning death, the possum is anything but playing. Under most circumstances, a threatened possum will bear its (surprisingly large) teeth with a hiss or screech. However, faced with a dire enough threat, it up and "dies."

It drops into a near-coma. Its tongue lolls, eyes open but vacant, and a foul green liquid leaks from its anus. It may take a possum upwards of four hours to come out of this apparently involuntary biochemical state.

It's perhaps little wonder that the possum should be so good at imitating death, because death lurks around every corner for this species. Due to heavy predation, and a predilection for becoming road kill, possums typically live only a measly two years in the wild, and even those living in captivity succumb to old age quickly.

And this death rate is despite a few startling immunities. Possums are highly resistant to pit viper (e.g. copperhead, water moccasin) venoms. Research suggests that possums – which will eat snakes, among many other things – are locked in an evolutionary arms race where they are constantly developing new ways to combat snake venom. They're highly resistant to rabies, likely as a result of a slightly lower body temperature that makes it difficult for the virus to thrive.

They also function as tick vacuums. A possum trundling through the undergrowth accumulates a large collection of ticks, but possums are such fastidious groomers that ticks which latch onto them are as good as dead. A dense possum population may even help reduce the prevalence of Lyme disease.

The possum is a consummate opportunist, exactly the sort of middleweight scavenger that thrives in the margins of human society. By all accounts, it is doing well: despite a near-total lack of real winter survival skills, it can be found as far north as southern Ontario. Global warming and the ceaseless march of human development only serve to prime the possum for further range expansion in the near future.

All things considered, the possum may not be the worst hanger-on for humanity to have. It provides a lesson in the extraordinary-as-ordinary. It's easy to disregard the sheer, magnificent oddity of this omnivore, but truth is stranger than fiction, and few truths are stranger than the Virginia opossum.

# Phoebes: To Thy Old Nest Be True

CAROLYN LORIÉ

While winter in New England can be stunningly beautiful, with its magical snowfalls and ethereal silences, I must admit that by mid-February the long absence of so many songbirds has me feeling bereft. I miss the vireos; I miss the thrushes; and, most especially, I miss the pair of phoebes that settles into the well-worn nest on the gable end of my house to raise their young.

It's amazing how two tiny beings weighing no more than a handful of twigs can evoke such strong emotions in me. I am joyful when the pair resurfaces in early spring. I'm moved by their devotion to their shared progeny, and I take pleasure in the companionship they provide one another.

But on some level I know that these are sentimental notions that I am ascribing to behavior that is biologically, not emotionally, driven. The phoebes I see one year aren't the same phoebes that I observed the previous year.

Or are they?

It turns out the mating habits of songbirds are far more complicated than I ever knew. No, emotions probably don't play into it (not theirs anyway). But my belief that I am being revisited by the same pair of birds year after year may not be so absurd, while my assumption that all the young that they tend are in fact their young may be inaccurate.

As Steven Hagenbuch, a conservation biologist with Audubon Vermont, explains, the process of songbird procreation generally follows a set pattern, but within that pattern there are quirks and there are exceptions.

For 90 percent of songbirds, including phoebes, the process goes like this: the male establishes a territory and then courts a female. That pair then build or find a nest, copulate, incubate their eggs, feed each other and their nestlings, and eventually, if all goes well, see off the fledglings. The departure of the young completes a breeding cycle, at which point the paired birds may stay together and produce another brood, or they might seek other mates and start the cycle anew. This, says Hagenbuch, is known as breeding cycle monogamy – one male, one female together for as long as it takes for a nest of baby birds to make it to independence.

But, he adds, even within this brief period of commitment, things get complicated. Social monogamy describes the shared behaviors outlined above, but the commitment here is not to the relationship between one male and one female – it's each bird's commitment to the propagation of its own genes.

To that end, both the male and female of a socially monogamous couple may copulate with multiple other partners. In fact, according to Kent McFarland, a conservation biologist with the Vermont Center for Ecostudies, most do. The female will add eggs fertilized by another male to the eggs she tends to with her steady partner. According to a study done by researchers at Purdue University, the first clutch of eggs produced by a pair of eastern phoebes will contain about nine percent of what is referred to as "extrapair young." If the pair stays together and produces a second clutch, the percentage of extrapair eggs increases.

These seeming transgressions do not disrupt the enterprise at hand, namely the raising of young. The original couple will proceed as planned, tending to a batch of nestlings that may be genetically mixed.

As for long-term pair bonds, that kind of fidelity just isn't part of the songbird world. There is nothing to suggest that songbirds look for last year's mate. There is, however, site fidelity, meaning birds will return to the same site where they successfully nested the year before.

Which brings us back to my phoebes.

They are among the species of birds that will seek out the same site for multiple years, says McFarland. And researchers have discovered that, because of this commitment to place, sometimes the same male and the same female that jointly raised a brood or two the year before will find each other again.

So, will last year's phoebes that nested in my yard be among those that reattach? Maybe, maybe not. Will all the nestlings whose fleshy heads pop up at feeding time be the product of the pair tending them? I'll never know.

Ultimately, it doesn't matter. The particulars of my phoebes' mating habits won't change how I feel about them. This spring, as the snow melts and the air warms, I will see the phoebes anew and start my own cycle of welcoming them back, observing their behavior, rooting for their young, and then mourning their inevitable departure.

# march

# 1 first week

Days are longer, the sun is stronger, and turkey vultures are here, seeking roadkill. They prefer to eat animals soon after they have died but they can metabolize bacterial toxins, allowing them to feed on carrion in a fairly advanced state of decay. Other scavengers are turned off sooner.

Black, withered stalks of last year's Indian pipes may still be erect.

Most of last year's cattails have broken off, adding material to the soil at their feet.

# second week 2

Short-tailed weasels are showing brown around the eyes and mouths, as pelage turns from winter white to summer brown.

The distress call of the male wood duck – a loud whoo eek, whoo eek – sounds more like an angry woodpecker than a duck.

High water spilling into floodplains means good feeding for migratory waterfowl.

Chickadees prefer birdhouses that are in or near woods. On their own they use rotten stubs, tree cavities, and abandoned woodpecker holes.

# third week

Pairs of hooded mergansers are working their way north,
diving for minnows in ponds and in the quieter parts of rivers.

Early phoebes are singing.
People who don't love phoebes might not call it singing.

Nerves and blood vessels in the tip of a woodcock's bill allow it
to sense odors and movements as it probes deeply into the soil.
As soon as the ground thaws, woodcocks will be there.

Ravens may be seen now carrying building materials to the construction site.

# fourth week

Humans often mistake grouse drumming for an engine of some sort and,
strange as it may seem, grouse may mistake one of our engines for a grouse.
They'll sometimes stay nearby when someone is mowing the lawn.

Gray squirrels are born, usually in a nest
high in a hardwood tree.

Gray comma butterflies may fly on warm days.
They overwintered as adults, and commas in this first generation
don't need flowers, preferring rotten fruit, carrion, tree sap, and dung.

# Tasty Teas (and More) From Trees: Black and Yellow Birch

RUSS COHEN

Scratch and then sniff a black or yellow birch twig, and the pleasant aroma will likely put a smile on your face. What you are smelling is oil of wintergreen (methyl salicylate). This chemical compound is present in the inner bark in both species, although typically to a greater degree in black birch. In the trees, as well as several edible berries that grow in our region, the compound serves as a defense against herbivorous insects. Most people, however, enjoy the taste.

You can make a very nice wintergreen-flavored tea from peeled black or yellow birch twigs. I advise against trying to brew this the traditional way, though (i.e., steeping twigs in boiling water). The reason is that oil of wintergreen is volatile and easily driven off by heat, so if you attempt to make tea with hot water, your kitchen will smell great but there will likely be little if any flavor in your tea cup.

Here's my recommended method: get a couple of quart-sized, wide-mouth Mason jars. Peel about three dozen twigs. A carrot peeler works well for this, but a sturdy pocket knife should also do the trick. Fill the jars with cool-to-lukewarm water, then add as many of the peeled twigs, and the peelings from those twigs, that you have the patience to cram into the jars. The more you put in, the stronger the flavor.

Put lids on the jars and wait. While I used to think that you needed to put the jars in the sun for a day or two, and slow-brew, I have since found that just letting the jars sit around, unrefrigerated, for several hours is enough to ensure strong flavor.

If you're not a tea drinker, there are other ways to enjoy that wintergreen taste. Simply chewing on a twig is pleasant, and if you're camping and have forgotten your tooth brush, you can use black or yellow birch as a natural toothbrush and breath freshener. This is not as far a stretch as it sounds: xylitol, another compound in both species, contributes sweetness and reduces the number of bacteria that cause tooth decay. It's an ingredient that appears in some varieties of toothpastes, mouthwashes, and chewing gum.

Birch – not just yellow or black, but other species such as paper birch – can be tapped just like sugar maples. Birch sap typically starts to flow just after the sugar maples have ended their run. Many years ago, I tapped some black birch trees on my family's land and I got about one gallon of sap per hour per tap from the trees. Unfortunately, birch sap is even more diluted than maple sap, and I had to boil the heck out of it to get anything. What I eventually got didn't have any oil of wintergreen flavor; it looked and tasted very similar to molasses.

Another use for birch is as a natural pain killer. Methyl salicylate is related to salicylic acid, the active ingredient in aspirin, and it has a similar pain-killing effect (in fact, methyl salicylate is one of the active ingredients in Bengay liniment). So, if you are out in the woods this spring and twist your ankle, consider chewing on a black or yellow birch twig. At the very least, the taste will distract you from the pain, and you'll limp home with fresh breath.

# Hearing a Peep

Kent P. McFarland

It's a warm evening, and the only signs of snow are the eroding piles beside the driveway. Down in the valley, there is a chorus erupting, and up on the hill in a pond, another is just beginning to call. The spring peepers are in stereo. Spring has finally sprung.



The cacophony is emanating from hundreds of male spring peepers. Each peep is made when a frog forces air from its lungs, over the vocal cords in the larynx, and into an air sac in its throat. The air enters the sac from openings on each side of the mouth cavity, causing the sac to balloon outward. The inflated sac acts as a sounding board, amplifying the sound and carrying it from the frog to my ears across the valley.

What sounds like chaos to me sounds organized to a peeper. Several males may interact vocally by forming duets, trios, or quartets, with alternating peep calls and individual notes. When males alternate calls, one individual, the follower, usually calls within 40 to 70 milliseconds from the end of the leader's call.

Males tend to stay within a close pitch range of each other. The spacing and timing of calls accentuates the distinctiveness of each male's call so that it is not lost in the overall din and allows a female to zero in on a single calling male. When another male frog moves too close, one male may use a second type of call, a trill. The trill seems to reflect a higher degree of aggression than the peep call and will stimulate one of the individuals either to move away or perhaps to trill back in challenge, causing a trill-off. A trill-off can escalate into a brief physical scuffle, with the winner staying and the loser moving on to quieter waters.

Each male peeper can pump out from 3,000 to 4,000 peeps an hour for several hours each night. So it is not surprising that male trunk muscles, which help propel air from the lungs, average 15 percent of their body mass compared to only 3 percent for the quiet females. Aerobic capacity of trunk muscle is six times that of leg muscles, and in males is 17 times greater than that of female trunk muscle. Peepers derive about 90 percent of their energy for call production from fat reserves in these muscles. Males weigh on average about the same as two dimes, yet their sound pressure is comparable to the song of a warbler (about four quarters in weight) or a blackbird (a whopping eight half-dollars in weight). These little peepers have big bellows.

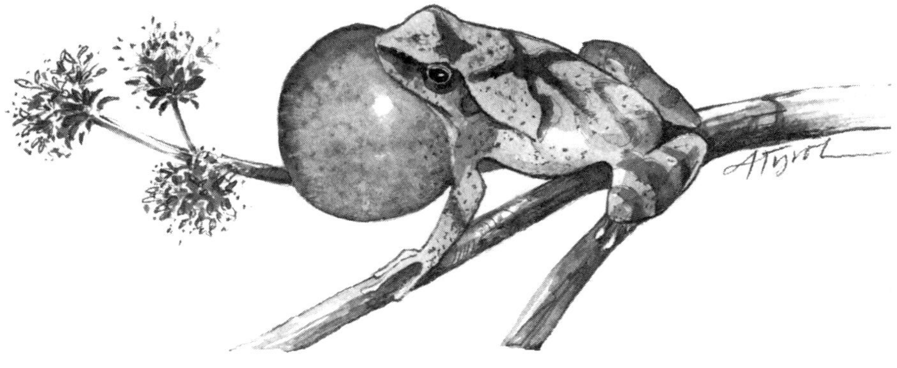

The peeper mating system is based on female choice. The louder and faster he peeps, the better his chances of attracting a receptive female. When biologists played recorded peep calls for female peepers, the females preferred peep rates double those found in the wild, indicating a strong sexual selection for males that can peep fast. Male peepers, therefore, push their singing abilities to the limit, performing at or close to their full physiological capacity. But one night of binge calling doesn't seem to wear them out: males that have the higher peep rates in one night tend to have higher peep rates every night.

The evening temperature can affect calling patterns. On warmer evenings, peepers call much more frequently. The consumption of oxygen increases with calling rate, which in turn increases with temperature. At a balmy 60 degrees, peep calls are repeated up to 13,500 times per night.

Not all males sing, though. A big chorus of singers will also attract a host of silent males, who mix in around the edges. These shy guys tend to be smaller than the big singers. They quietly wait near a good singer, watching for a female that may be attracted to a peeping male. When she comes along, they use their quickness and agility to beat the singer to the female.

According to the *Vermont Amphibian and Reptile Atlas*, peepers can begin calling as early as March 15, with peak activity in early May. Chances are good that the spring peeper chorus is now happening earlier than in the past, according to a study by James Gibbs, from the State University of New York in Syracuse, and Alvin Breisch, of the New York Department of Environmental Conservation.

From 1900 to 1912, Albert Wright, an instructor in zoology at Cornell University, visited ponds around the campus daily each spring to record the date of the first calls of frogs. Ninety years later, volunteers collected the same kind of information for the *New York Amphibian and Reptile Atlas*, allowing Gibbs and Breisch a chance to compare. Wright, on average, heard his first peepers on April 4. Atlas volunteers heard them around March 20, about 13 days earlier.

# The Early Buzz on Honeybees

MARY HOLLAND

For some, spring begins with the flow of maple sap, or maybe the arrival of robins or redwing blackbirds. For inveterate gardeners, the new season never really starts until the soil can be turned.

The arrival of honeybees in fields and orchards is an obvious sign of spring, and during this time of year honeybees, both domesticated and feral, move about in their hives preparing to head out for the flowers.

In fact, things begin picking up in honeybee hives long before the snow starts melting. In some colonies the queen begins laying eggs as early as mid-winter. As larvae hatch, worker bees must get moving to feed them.

A colony of honeybees soon becomes crowded and busy. It might include tens of thousands of workers (unfertilized females) and several hundred drones (males), but only one queen (fertile female). Each class of bees has a task: the drones mate with queens; the queens lay eggs; and the workers build and maintain the hive. As spring advances, the workers also collect food to feed the queen and the young bees.

Most species of social insects – including hornets, paper wasps, bumblebees, and yellow jackets – have near-complete die-offs as winter approaches. With the exception of a colony's queen, who hibernates in a rotting log or other protected area, all members of these species succumb in fall. In early spring, their queen emerges from hibernation and begins laying eggs to rebuild the colony.

Honeybees are different. Their workers spend spring, summer, and fall storing food, so the queen and the workers can survive all winter. The drones that mate with the queen immediately expire. The remaining drones are tolerated and cared for in the hive until fall, when they're escorted from the hive and left to die. Their departure can assure that the workers and queen have enough food in the hive for winter.

There are other forms of helpful population controls.

By fall, the queen begins laying fewer eggs at a time and the older bees begin to die off. That means that a summertime colony population of up to 60,000 might drop to 10,000 by winter.

As winter approaches and temperatures drop, honeybees bunch together in their hives to conserve heat. The bees in the outer layer of the cluster compress tightly into a shell, which helps insulate those inside. The bees inside the cluster then use their wing muscles to shiver, causing an increased metabolic rate that releases heat for the whole cluster. Winter temperatures on the outside edge of the cluster may hover around 40 degrees, while the inner layer warms to 75 degrees.

In a warm cluster the queen can move about, laying the eggs that will become the spring foragers. The workers are busy, too, shifting their positions to cover new areas of the honeycomb to find food. The honeybees require some help from the weather: they need above-freezing days so they can go outside to void excrement. They also need warm breaks, because a prolonged spell of extreme cold can inhibit cluster movement and cause starvation – even though the bees are only inches from a meal.

What's on the honeybee menu? Nectar and pollen. Nectar, the sweet liquid from plants, is stored as honey after undergoing evaporation and the action of enzymes introduced by the bees. Nectar and pollen are collected well into fall – until the last goldenrod and asters succumb to frost.

The work of wild bees has been a source of sweetness and plant pollination for humans for centuries. Cave paintings in Egypt indicate that people were harvesting honey 8,000 years ago from wild hives. Although today most honeybees come from man-made hives, swarms of these bees occasionally escape into the wild to begin homesteading inside a hollow tree or similar shelter.

Sometime next month, the honeybees of northern New England will begin leaving their hives to find food. Temperature will be key: the mercury must reach 45 or 50 degrees for honeybees' flight muscles to operate. Few if any wildflowers or garden flowers will be in blossom when the bees take flight, but they will find food in other places – early-flowering shrubs or trees, such as poplar, willow, alder, or beaked hazelnut.

By late April, honeybees will be buzzing among dandelions, chickweed, coltsfoot, and mustard.

# Accipiters: The Motorcycle Hawks

STEVEN D. FACCIO

I was enjoying a morning cup of coffee in the sunroom when I saw the hawk. It was perched across the road, maybe 30 yards away, its chest puffed up against the cold. It appeared to be eyeing the activity at our birdfeeder. As I was trying to decide if it was a female sharp-shinned hawk or a male Cooper's hawk, the bird launched from its perch, and in an instant had threaded its way through a dense tangle of road-side branches while in hot pursuit of a blue jay. It all happened so quickly that I wasn't even sure if the jay had been captured, although I was able to identify the predator as a Cooper's hawk.

The Cooper's hawk is one of three North American species in the genus *Accipiter*, along with the smaller sharp-shinned hawk and the larger northern goshawk. The silhouettes of this trio look like a set of nesting cookie cutters, each with the same basic shape, differing only in size. As I witnessed, accipiters are sit-and-wait, stealth predators, capable of quick bursts of speed and exceptional maneuverability – much like a motorcycle racing down a winding mountain road.

The motorcycle hawks are bird-hunters and, according to the Latin meaning of the word accipiter, they are also the "true hawks." They are the nemeses of other birds large and small, chasing down their avian prey in short bursts of speed. As Pete Dunne points out in his classic book *Hawks in Flight*, "...the true hawk is a sprinter. If prey is not taken in the first attempt or after a short chase, pursuit is broken off. Surprise is the ally of an accipiter, not endurance."

If surprise is their ally, then acceleration and maneuverability are their weapons. An accipiter's long rudder of a tail provides the precise cornering ability needed to follow the twisting and turning escape flight of smaller birds. The speed to overtake its passerine prey is provided by rounded wings, which catch enough air to generate a quick burst of speed, while short wing length allows the accipiter to slip through dense woodlands without crashing into branches.

Or so it might seem.

Surprisingly, a study lead by Aaron Roth of Northeastern University, which examined 339 skeletal specimens of accipiters from museum collections, found that nearly 20 percent had healed fractures of the pelvic girdle, primarily to the wishbone. While it's easy to imagine that dashing through dense vegetation at high rates of speed in pursuit of other birds is a rather dangerous lifestyle, and that impact injuries are likely to occur, it is surprising that such a high proportion of accipiters are able to recover from broken bones, especially considering the importance of flight to their hunting style.

The smallest member of this trio, the sharp-shinned hawk, occupies the narrowest niche. These compact bundles of energy primarily capture small, sparrow-size birds. That said, when the opportunity presents itself, they can be more ambitious. I once saw a "sharpie" take a blue jay, a bird nearly equal in size, but which the hawk must have out-weighed two to one.

# Beware of Encroaching Forests

CHUCK WOOSTER

One February, while taking advantage of an open winter to cut brush around the edges of our pasture, I thought back to one of my favorite lectures in college. The professor was a Maine native teaching a course on New England history. Leaning sternly over the podium, he warned us students about the dangers of living in the woods. He reminded us that the trees were constantly growing, even at night while we slept. That the forests were forever encroaching and threatening to wipe out the fragile beachhead of fields and pastures that we humans had labored for centuries to establish here in New England. That eternal vigilance was required, and that preemptively cutting trees whenever possible was the only way to protect our heritage and ensure our future.

The class, tree-huggers by and large, many hailing from non-New England states, sat as if struck by a falling limb. Only those sitting in the front row, or those with a taste for this sort of thing, noticed the twinkle in the professor's eye.

He was right, of course, ecologically speaking. We live in the woods here in northern New England; forests are the defining feature of our ecological niche. If we halted our clearing and haying, paving and grading, logging and lawn mowing, the woods would swallow us whole within a century.

In fact, over the past century, they nearly did. Vermont was three-quarters deforested in the middle 1800s; now it's three-quarters the other way. According to U.S. Forest Service data, Maine is the most heavily forested state in the nation, with nearly 90 percent of its acres in woodland, followed closely by New Hampshire at 84 percent. Vermont picks up the bronze with 78 percent, though New York would certainly be on the podium if only the Adirondacks region of the state were counted. We live in the woods.

That's true in another way, as well: Vermont is the most rural state in the nation, with 62 percent of the population living outside of urban centers (as defined by the U.S. Census Bureau). Maine is second with 60 percent. New Hampshire is well down the list at 41 percent, but if you stripped off the seacoast, it would certainly rise to the top tier of rural performers.

Many of us are surprised to learn that our states are so rural; places like Alaska or Wyoming typically come first to mind. But here's the crucial distinction: rural means that people live in small towns, not that a state is sparsely populated. Wyoming is actually a relatively urbanized state, with only 35 percent of its population living in small towns – even while it is also among the most sparsely populated. Rural means a village green, a church with steeple, a post office, a store with a few gas pumps, in short, communities where everybody knows everybody else.

And in New England rural means people living in the woods. Not nearby the woods or within an hour's drive of the woods, but in the actual woods. It's easy to forget that no other part of the country is quite like this.

We may even fail to realize how wooded our New England landscape is because, for most of us most of the time, we spend our days in the cleared areas: among the buildings, roads, lawns, and pastures where we live much of our lives. The woods can fade into the background, except perhaps during autumn foliage season, and recede from our consciousness. We're like kids who, having grown up in inland towns without ever having set eyes on the ocean, can be forgiven for still believing, at some level, that most of the world must be dry land.

Back on our farm, a half-century of mechanical haying has allowed saplings and small trees to slowly creep in from the old stone walls, gradually extending the forest's hold. Few farmers want to snag a sickle bar or cutting head on a sapling or stump, so year by year, as the seedlings creep in, the hayable field is reduced. An occasional intervention is required if you want to reverse this process, and winters with very little snowfall are the perfect time to do this.

I've been able to cut the larger trees and saplings right at ground level, preparing the ground for brush hogging in the spring. I figure I'll be able to push the woods back by an average of 20 feet over a 1,000-foot treeline, which will amount to just under a half-acre of new field and pasture. Very satisfying work.

You might think, after all this, that I'm anti-woods. Not at all; I spend as much time in the woods as I can. It's just that our farm is 78 percent wooded, and I'm mindful of my former professor's advice that eternal vigilance is the price of pasture.

# Coyotes: Listening to Tricksters

Brian R. Mitchell

As the sunset colors fade from purple to black, the forest is dimly illuminated by a first-quarter moon. An eerie sound breaks the calm. It is not the long, low, slow howling of wolves that can be heard further north, but the group yip-howl of coyotes: short howls that often rise and fall in pitch, punctuated with staccato yips, yaps, and barks.

When people hear coyote howls, they often mistakenly assume that they're hearing a large pack of animals, all raising their voices at once. But this is an auditory illusion called the "beau geste" effect. Because of the variety of sounds produced by each coyote, and the way sound is distorted as it passes through the environment, two of these tricksters can sound like seven or eight animals.

Group yip-howls are produced by a mated and territorial pair of "alpha" coyotes, with the male howling while the female intersperses her yips, barks, and short howls. "Beta" coyotes (the children of the alpha pair from previous years) and current-year pups may join in if they are nearby, or respond with howls of their own. And once one group of coyotes starts howling, chances are that any other alpha pairs nearby will respond in kind, with chorus after chorus of group yip-howls rippling across the miles.

I spent seven years studying coyote vocal communication during my dissertation research at the University of California, Berkeley. While eastern coyotes are a larger and distinct subspecies from the western coyotes that I worked with, the basic findings of my research and the work done by others applies to all coyotes. Coyotes have sometimes been called "song dogs," and their long distance songs come in two basic types.

The first, the group yip-howl, is thought to have the dual purpose of promoting bonding within the family group while also serving as a territorial display. In other words, the coyotes are saying "we're a happy family, and we own this turf so you'd better keep out." In a sense, the group howls create an auditory fence around a territory, supplementing the physical scent marks left by the group.

Coyotes will also howl and bark separately. This second type of song is virtually always an indication of disturbance or agitation, and in my experience, the higher the proportion of howls, the more agitated the coyote is. Coyotes will howl and bark at neighbors who intrude on their territory, and at dogs, people, and other large animals that they perceive as potential threats.

My research documented that coyote barks and howls are individually specific. Much like we can tell people apart by their voices, there is enough information in coyote vocalizations for me (OK, my computer if you want to get technical) to tell individuals apart. If, as I suspect, coyotes can distinguish each other by their song, it would not be analogous to the animals constantly shouting their own names; it would be more akin to our ability to recognize Marlon Brando because of the distinctive timbre and cadence of his voice. Characteristics including dominant pitch, duration, how quickly howls rise and fall in pitch, and tendency to "warble" while howling all distinguish one coyote from another.

For howls, this individual distinctiveness does not fade with distance. I was able to record and identify individual coyotes over a distance of greater than one mile. Given their keen hearing, it is likely coyotes can discern individual howls at much greater distances - three miles or more on a calm night.

Barks, on the other hand, degrade quickly over distance, with the higher frequencies fading first. This makes it theoretically possible for coyotes familiar with an individual (say, a mate or family group member) to determine roughly how far away that individual is, based on the proportion of high frequencies in the barks.

Imagine a scenario where a lone coyote is patrolling the territory boundary and comes across an intruder. He starts barking and howling, and his mate and beta children come running to the right place, because his howls indicate how agitated he is, and his barks allow his family to pinpoint the direction and distance to his location. Although I was not able to prove that coyotes can do these tasks, the information needed is present in their calls and there are strong evolutionary advantages to learning how to use it.

We still have much to learn about coyote vocal communication. Even after years of studying coyote calls, I was barely able to scratch the surface. These tricksters hold their secrets tightly.

# april

APR

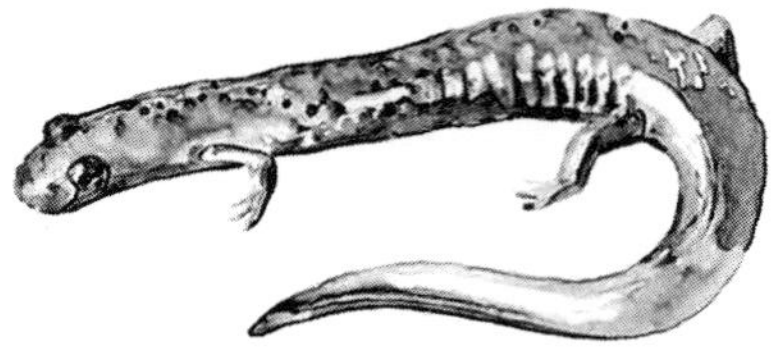



## 1 first week

Later in spring otters add frogs, salamanders, and baby ducks to the menu. Fish and crayfish are top choices year-round.

April 1: Skunks are active now, but don't worry, it'll be another week before there's any odor to their spray.

The tiny, brilliantly purple female flowers of beaked hazelnut are open, and the male catkins are shedding pollen.

If it's warm, there may be a lot of "firsts" this week: first phoebe, tree swallow, kestrel, and/or chipmunk.

## second week 2

By now ruby-throated hummingbirds have reached New Jersey.

Returning robins will feed on last summer's rose hips when worms are scarce.

After spending the winter in the soil, white pine weevils are ascending to the terminal shoots of their host trees to feed and lay eggs.

The genus name for trailing arbutus, *Epigaea*, is derived from the Greek word meaning "upon the ground," which is where you should look for this small, sweet scented wildflower.

## third week

Many wind-pollinated trees – quaking aspen, balsam poplar, big-toothed aspen, willow, elm, boxelder, and red maple – are in flower.

On rainy nights when the temperature is above 41 degrees, spring peepers migrate to their breeding ponds. The males may stay for a month, but most females arrive, mate, lay eggs, and leave within a couple of days.

Tree swallow probably aren't really showing off, but they look as though they are as they skim ponds for insects.

## fourth week

Queen bumblebees fly in a zigzag course close to the ground searching for a nest site. A single queen will begin a new colony, often in an abandoned mouse nest.

Sometimes flickers all seem to arrive on the same day.

When the water temperature reaches 50 degrees, perch begin to spawn.

First of perhaps three litters of northern short-tailed shrews is born. This common shrew has a poisonous bite and preys on mice and voles that are larger than it is.

# April Fool's: Nature Myths and Misbeliefs

Michael J. Caduto

Walking through the woods on a cool spring morning, I saw a barred owl in an old maple tree. I circled the owl three times from a distance. Its head kept turning to follow me, tracking my movements with three complete revolutions.

One of the owl's chicks had fallen from the nest, so I climbed the tree and placed the chick back in it. Then the owl flew up and pushed the chick out of the nest onto the ground, where it lay in a pile of melting snow.

I noticed that the maple was the biggest tree in sight, so it had to be the oldest. A rusty sap bucket hung from the tree on a tap that had probably been forgotten some fifteen years earlier. The bucket, which had originally been placed four feet off the ground, was now ten feet high, having been moved up as the tree grew.

A cute baby skunk was hiding in a hollow under the tree. I stuck my head in to have a good look, because I knew that immature skunks can't spray. Then I saw a porcupine, but when I drew closer, it shot several quills at me, narrowly missing my neck.

Walking home, I heard a bear off in the distance. It had just emerged from hibernation and was hooting to find a mate.

I passed a fallen tree and contemplated how it must have landed silently because no one had been there to hear it.

When I got home, I looked at the calendar and noticed the date: April 1.

This fictional account is spun of common misbeliefs that are handed down through the generations with surprising tenacity. Here are some of these myths, followed by the corresponding truths. (Many thanks to the staff of the Springfield office of Vermont's Agency of Natural Resources for sharing their favorite nature misconceptions.)

*An owl can turn its head 360 degrees*: While it looks like an owl can spin its head around at will, in fact the head only moves up to 270 degrees in either direction. The structure of an owl's neck vertebrae and specially adapted blood vessels enable these extreme motions. (Red-tailed hawks can turn their heads nearly as far as owls.)

*If you touch a baby bird that has fallen from its nest, and then put it back, the parents will reject it and let it die*: Adults will not abandon a chick just because a human touched it. If you find a baby chick on the ground, search overhead for the nest and gently place the chick back in the nest. Many "baby birds" found on the ground are really fledglings who are learning to fly. If a juvenile bird has young feathers, is awkwardly flying near the ground, and can perch on your finger, then place it on a nearby branch and the parents will find it.

*The biggest trees are the oldest trees*: Growth rates depend on a combination of genetics and growing conditions. Some species (white pine, cottonwood) grow quickly, while others (white oak, hickory) grow more slowly. A red oak 16 inches in diameter that is growing in fertile soil with plenty of sunlight might be 50 years old, while a red oak of similar age that is competing with other trees in poor growing conditions might only be 10 inches across. A shagbark hickory growing nearby that is the same size could be 75 years old.

*A nail driven into a tree moves up as the tree grows*: Trees only grow upward from the tips of their branches. A nail or sugaring tap driven or drilled into the side of a tree will remain at the same height over time. The bole of a tree grows outward, so eventually the nail or hole will be engulfed by wood.

*Baby skunks can't spray*: Skunks can spray to a certain extent within a few weeks of being born, and can spray at full force at about three months old.

*Porcupines can shoot their quills*: A porcupine does not have ballistic quills. If you touch a porcupine, its sharp quills may penetrate your skin and separate from the animal. It's also capable of thwacking predators with its tail.

*Bears can hoot*: Black bear cubs moan, coo, mew, purr, bawl, and make gulping sounds. Adults grunt, bellow, and woof. On rare occasions, such as when cornered, bears growl. But they don't hoot. Owls hoot.

*If a tree falls in a forest and there is no one around to hear, it makes no sound*: Maybe. Maybe not. You're on your own for this one.

# Migrators Spring Forward with New Season

CHARLES W. JOHNSON

Early April is an unpredictable month in the North Country, a time for back-and-forth tag between the remnants of winter chill and spring warmth. Yet within the unpredictability there is certainty. The earliest flowers poke up, even bloom, right on schedule, in temperatures often well below freezing. The first migratory birds – red-winged blackbirds, robins, woodcocks, killdeers – return to these still-drab, snow-blotched landscapes within a day or two of their usual arrival times. Others, not just birds, will soon follow. And they don't always have far to travel.

APR

In the next few weeks, even before the snow melts completely, many amphibians will make their annual treks from hibernating locations in the ground or under logs to their ancestral waters and wetlands to breed. Some – wood frogs, spring peepers, and American toads – will sing to claim their territories and attract mates. Others, such as spotted salamanders, are not vocal, but they're visible – on warm rainy nights they move from their underground winter quarters over land to vernal pools in the forest. They come to pools by the hundreds to breed and leave eggs that will hatch into larvae that will grow into adults.

Later will come butterflies, many of which will sail and skip north to visit summer flowers, then work their way back south as the blossoms disappear. Red admirals and painted ladies, among others, will arrive from as far away as the southern United States, Mexico, Central America and the West Indies. Monarchs will travel north from an isolated 50-acre forest stand in central Mexico, breeding and fanning out as they come, until they occupy milkweed-bearing meadows across the eastern United States and Canada. The last of these northernmost broods will be the ones to re-trace their progenitors' flight down to Mexico.

Some bats, such as the hoary and silver-haired bats, come north from southern regions, keeping pace with the emergence of flying insects, their source of food; while others, such as the little brown, big brown, and Keene's bat, begin emerging from hibernation in caves and attics throughout the region.

Aquatic animals migrate, too. Atlantic salmon, alewives, and American shad swim from the ocean up rivers and streams to spawn in shallow headwaters in the Northeast.

The movement is not all horizontal or latitudinal: crows begin shifting their range in spring from lowlands to higher elevations, while moose go the opposite direction, moving from hills and mountains to wetlands. As the coastal waters of New England warm, lobsters move in from the deep.

These mass movements, repeated twice annually over eons, usually occur along the same routes, and thus become vulnerable to obstacles that humans put in their way. We have a long history of doing so. Hunters in New England, in boats, picked off millions of flightless, helpless great auks as they swam close to shore on 3,000-mile migrations between the Caribbean and the North Atlantic, helping lead to their extinction in 1845. Whalers of generations past pursued their giant quarry worldwide, intercepting them in this region as they moved through the Gulf of Maine on their way between summer's arctic waters and the winter's Caribbean breeding and calving grounds – bringing several species to near extinction, all for oil to fuel lamps or lubricate gears.

Dams barred salmon and shad from entry into major New England rivers for spawning, while lake sturgeon, the largest and one of the most ancient of freshwater fish, could no longer swim up tributaries of Lake Champlain to lay eggs. Oceanside development and recreation on beaches eliminated breeding sites for many migratory shorebirds.

Cars and trucks have squashed untold numbers of crossing amphibians, while millions, perhaps billions, of migrating butterflies end up splashed on windshields and grills. Night-migrating birds hit towers and city skyscrapers in numbers that stagger the imagination (I once picked up 3,000 dead birds, of many species, which had struck guy wires of just three radio towers in a single foggy night during a fall migration).

Even if the animals survive these perilous journeys, other threats await at their destinations. Heavy cutting in tropical and temperate forests has severely reduced the numbers of many migratory birds that depend on both. The small mountain sanctuary of monarchs in Mexico is under siege from human neighbors who also need forest trees and brush for fuel. Closer to home, vandals have been known to kill roosting bats in caves, including Vermont's Dorset Bat Cave at Mt. Aeolus, which is considered the largest bat over-wintering site in New England.

On the other hand, we have taken significant strides toward protection. We work to protect migratory bird species, build fish-ways around dams, restrict areas where beach birds nest, and we have placed bars across cave entrances during bat hibernation. We do things that would have been unthinkable a generation ago: in my town, volunteers go out with headlamps on rainy spring nights, and with wet hands scoop up salamanders and carry them safely across roads.

Yes, living things are on the move now, and they need our help, in small ways and big, as they try to reach their new homes.

For a fun spring activity related to this essay, turn to page 202.

# Clams in the Woods

SUSAN SHEA

Clambakes, fried clams, clam diggers, clam shacks – we usually associate clams with the ocean. You may have also seen freshwater clams in rivers and lakes. But did you know there are clams that live in the woods?

In our region, there are several species of fingernail clams that inhabit vernal pools, the temporary woodland pools where frogs and salamanders lay their eggs in the spring. As temperatures warm and melting snow and rain fill depressions in the forest floor, these small clams, only the size and shape of a child's fingernail, become active.

A fingernail clam moves slowly along the murky bottom of a vernal pool and burrows in the mud by extending and contracting its foot, a muscular appendage. To breathe, it extracts oxygen from the water with gills. An efficient filter-feeder, the clam sucks up the rich soup of the pool through a tubular siphon, filtering out food particles, namely algae and bits of leaf litter that were broken down by other leaf-eaters. Wastewater is expelled from another siphon.

Late in the spring, usually in June, fingernail clams reproduce. According to Steve Faccio, a conservation biologist with the Vermont Center for Ecostudies, "the sheer number of fingernail clams can be dramatic at this time. Thousands of these young clams may cover the bottoms of pools and you can scoop up dozens in a handful."

Fingernail clams are hermaphrodites: both male and female sex organs are found in the same individual, explained Jim Kellogg, an aquatic biologist with the Vermont Department of Environmental Conservation. The eggs are fertilized and tiny clams grow inside the parent until they are released. Kellogg described opening a fingernail clam and seeing the little clams inside.

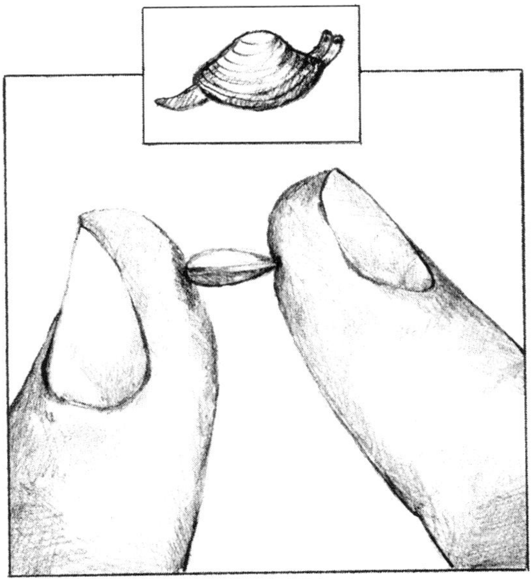

When summer comes and vernal pools dry up, the young clams burrow deep down in the muck and enter diapause – their development is put on hold. However, if the pool refills with water from autumn rains, the clams will become active again.

They follow the same strategy to survive the winter. Fingernail clams have been found overwintering as deep as eight inches underground, having dug more than 16 times their body length.

According to Faccio, fingernail clams are common in vernal pools in both Vermont and New Hampshire, especially in pools with a lot of leaf litter. He has found them in pools beneath a sunny, open woodland canopy and in pools in dense, dark forest. Some species also inhabit other temporary wetlands and even roadside ditches. Kellogg says that fingernail clams need adequate levels of calcium in the bedrock and soil to build their shells, and are usually found in water of at least a neutral pH. However, they are not as fussy as other freshwater clams in this respect, and he has found a few living under slightly acidic conditions.

These tiny clams provide food for other residents of vernal pools, such as snails, and visitors like salamanders, raccoons, and shorebirds. No one knows for sure how they disperse to other vernal pools. They cannot move very far on their own. One theory is that the clams attach to the fur or feathers of mink, ducks, or other travelers, and hitch a ride to other pools. Another idea is that ducks feeding on vegetation in vernal pools accidentally ingest the clams and later regurgitate or eliminate them whole in a different location.

Look for fingernail clams this spring in woodland vernal pools. Put your hand in the water and lift up a few of the dead leaves on the bottom, watching for glossy off-white shells. Or, if you're walking in the woods next fall and come upon little clamshells in the dry leaf litter, make a note of the location. Chances are, come spring, a vernal pool will appear there.

# Sweet and Sour Gardening

Chuck Wooster

Now is the time of year for cleaning out the woodstove and spreading the ashes on the garden, a chore that both prepares the stove for summer vacation and sweetens the soil for the coming growing season. Those without access to wood ash usually make the trek to the hardware store for a bag of lime, which also sweetens the soil, though without the benefit of the added potassium in wood ash.

Why do we need to keep adding ashes or lime to our soils, year after year? Weren't plants growing just fine hereabouts back before the days of lime and fertilizer?



Yes and no.

In relatively wet and humid parts of the globe, a description that includes the Northeast, soils tend to be acidic for the simple reason that calcium, the key ingredient in lime and ashes that adjusts pH, is a relatively soluble element that washes away over time. The underlying bedrock may be rich in calcium, but the constant action of rainwater and snowmelt washes the calcium into our rivers (and eventually into the oceans, where it becomes a key ingredient in shells, marine life, and coral reefs).

Our native vegetation, therefore, tends to flourish in (or at least tolerate) somewhat acidic conditions. But over the past century, the emissions that we've been adding to the atmosphere from the combustion of coal, oil, and natural gas, have led to acid rain, which may be 100 times more acidic than natural rainfall. This increased acidity accelerates the natural leaching of calcium, which has caused our soils to acidify as calcium is removed faster than it can be replaced from the bedrock.

The situation is troublesome for our native vegetation but is acute in the garden, where many of our favored plants are not native to the Northeast and were never accustomed to growing under acidic conditions in the first place. Tomatoes and asparagus – two heroes of the New England garden – come immediately to mind.

Many gardeners, seeing their tomatoes and asparagus suffering, apply fertilizer to try to rejuvenate their plants. But if the soil pH is too low, the fertilizer has no effect because the acidity has locked up the nutrition in a form that the plants can't use. The fertilizer runs off the garden, unused, a waste of money and a source of pollution to ponds and brooks. Meanwhile, the plants starve amidst plenty.

So a key spring task for every home gardener (and lawn-grower, too) is to ensure that soil pH is correct before fertilizing and planting. There are fancy test kits available for the job and state laboratories that will analyze your soil for a nominal fee. But there's an even easier way to at least see if you have a problem: indicator plants.

Is there moss growing in your garden, lawn, or orchard? Reach for the lime. Mosses grow beautifully in acidic soils and are a certain sign that your vegetables, grass, or apples are suffering. Look in the thin patches in the lawn or around the edges of the garden to make sure this low pH indicator isn't staring you in the face.

A second indicator, found more often in the orchard or pasture or rougher sections of the lawn, is wild strawberry, which looks just like cultivated strawberry only with much smaller leaves and fruit. Strawberries are very competitive on acidic soils and indicate that most other garden plants will not do well nearby.

Cultivated strawberries, of course, are also a desirable garden species. Serious gardeners will sometimes establish a lime-free section of the garden for growing strawberries and two other acid-loving plants: potatoes and carrots.

Are your potatoes routinely covered with scab? This could indicate that the pH is too high, not necessarily for tomatoes and asparagus, but certainly for spuds. Another indicator is carrots that are more woody than sweet. Many gardeners recall the carrots from their first year's garden as far tastier than anything they've managed to grow subsequently. It's not just that memories sweeten with age; it's that lime is bad for carrots.

A final thought on sweet soils: they're called "sweet" because that's how they taste. Back before the days of fancy soil tests, farmers and gardeners would put a pinch of soil in their mouths to gauge the acidity. Soils that tasted sour required lime; soils that tasted sweet were ready to go. I've always aspired to impressing people with this skill, but lacking the years of careful practice and calibration, I've never been able to produce meaningful data. The only response I've been able to muster, standing in front of my expectant friends with a thin ribbon of mud running down my chin, is "tastes kind of gritty."

# Season's Greetings From Your Neighborhood Skunk

KENT P. MCFARLAND

There is nothing like the fresh smell of a spring morning, unless, during the night, a skunk skulked about your neighborhood. The striped skunk is armed with just a teaspoon of odoriferous oil in its two anal glands, but a little bit goes a long way.

When I was in junior high, I was hit with a burst of spray from a skunk at close range. I can attest that at high concentrations it causes nausea. It also acts like tear gas, causing watering eyes and a running nose. Oh, and your mother will most definitely make you take your clothes off outside and throw them out. If you're lucky, she'll let you back in after a series of home remedies, which never seem to fully cure the stench.

Skunk oil research has been going on for over a century as scientists have tried to determine what makes the stuff so potent that it can drive a bear away. Way back in 1896, Thomas Aldridge at Johns Hopkins University showed that humans could detect the smell at just 10 parts per billion, the equivalent of detecting just one drop of it diluted into a medium-sized, backyard swimming pool. More recently, William Wood, a chemist from Humboldt State University, pointed out that a number of chemicals have been incorrectly attributed to the composition of skunk oil over the years, and his work has now given us a fairly complete understanding of those chemical compounds that are involved and how to neutralize them.

The scent-gland secretion is a yellow oil composed primarily of volatile compounds known as thiols, and their derivatives. (A thiol is a compound distinguished by its sulfur-hydrogen bond.) Most of us immediately recognize the smell of ethanethiol, a common thiol that's added to propane so we can easily smell any leaks. Another thiol creates the "skunky" smell of beer after it has been exposed to ultraviolet light.

The thiol derivatives present in skunk oil are not particularly odoriferous, but they are easily converted to far more potent thiols when they react with water. For weeks after I was sprayed, I would give off the faint smell of skunk at basketball practice. Perhaps the thioacetate derivatives trapped in my hair reacted with the moisture from my sweat. I don't remember, but I wonder if my defenders backed off a bit affording me more scoring opportunities. The power of thiols.

Many people believe that tomato juice will neutralize the odor of a skunk, but human olfactory fatigue is a better explanation for the apparent disappearance of the odor. I could hardly smell the odor on my body after a few hours, but when a new nose came into range, its owner squealed with disgust. A tired nose will smell the tomatoes rather than the skunk.

You can neutralize the offensive thiols in skunk spray with the sulfonic acids found in most detergents. Oxidizers such as hydrogen peroxide and baking soda are mild enough to be used on pets, although they may create interestingly colored hair for some. For washing down your deck or trash can, try liquid laundry bleach.

The skunk smell is certainly memorable. Even decades later, the thought of that moment when the skunk turned and sprayed almost turns my stomach and brings tears to my eyes again. The skunks are reluctant to use their scent, though. With only enough for a half-dozen sprays at most, and a 10-day period required to manufacture more, skunks will only spray if they absolutely have to. In an attempt to avoid spraying, skunks often give a warning. First, they show their striped white back to warn you. This is followed by threat behaviors, like stomping with both front feet, sometimes charging forward, and then edging backwards dragging their feet and hissing. If all this fails, watch out.

Each spray gland has a nipple, and skunks can aim and direct the spray using highly coordinated muscles. A skunk can spray up to 25 feet and hit something fairly accurately up to 7 feet away. When there is a target, they can direct a fine stream right at the victim's face. When being chased, a skunk will instead emit a foul cloud for the predator to run into.

There is one predator that remains undeterred by the odiferous oil: the great-horned owl. The small size of the olfactory lobes in their brains suggests that they have a very poor sense of smell. Some individual owls can downright stink of skunk, a common complaint among wildlife rehabilitation workers. Their nests can even smell of their musky meals. But larger-lobed mammals quickly learn to avoid the white stripe in the night.

# The Bird That Broke the Sound Barrier

Li Shen

A distant motor thud-thud-thuds as if trying to start, then dies away. The noise repeats, and again dies off. I've been fooled by this sound, wondering who could be trying to start an engine in the middle of the woods. This mechanical noise, of course, is really the drumming of a male ruffed grouse.

People once thought that male grouse struck their wings on hollow logs to produce this low whumping, but better observation revealed something far more astonishing. The bird stands bolt upright on a log, leans back on his tail, and fans his wings vigorously – so rapidly, in fact, that the wings achieve the same speed as the sound waves generated by their passage through the air. This causes the sound waves to "pile up" into a penetrating shock wave, also known as a sonic boom. For a one-and-a-quarter-pound grouse to exert such force takes strength and perseverance. Novice males have been observed going through all the motions and not producing any sound at all.

With a bit of practice, you too can create a sonic boom. Take a bull whip and flail with all your might. If you're lucky, you'll be rewarded with an explosive crack. The whip moves in an up-and-down series of waves along its length that undulate with increasing speed as they approach the tip. By the time the wave motion reaches the whip's end, the tip is moving at the speed of sound and the crack is its sonic boom.

The rigors of drumming cause a male grouse to lose 10 percent of his body weight during the spring season. So why, one might ask, would a bird go to all this trouble? If you haven't already guessed, it's all to do with mating.

Grouse are secretive forest floor foragers that rely on cryptic coloration and the cover of dense thickets to evade a long list of predators, including foxes, coyotes, fishers, bobcats, owls, and hawks. They live solitary lives for the most part. When it's time to attract a mate, the male lacks a singing voice, and even if he had flashy colors, they would be lost amid the vegetation. However, the shock waves of drumming carry effectively through the forest.

Drumming advertises the male's presence to female grouse. It is also a territorial announcement that tells other males, "stay away – this territory is taken!" In good habitat, male grouse tend to space themselves so each defends an area of about 10 acres, allowing them sufficient resources to survive. This space overlaps the territories of several females that risk their safety in walking some distance to investigate the drumming males. Occasionally, less successful young males have been observed drumming at the edges of a dominant male's performance area, perhaps to take advantage of the influx of females. However, ruffed grouse do not form the communal display areas (or leks) characteristic of prairie grouse.

Loud self-advertisement is a risky business for a bird with many predators. The male grouse chooses his drumming site with care to reduce the chances of unwanted attention. His performance stage, be it a log (ideally 15 inches high and 20 to 40 feet long) or a rock, is situated under overhead branches to deter raptors. At one end of the stage is some form of escape cover, a root mass, some brush, or a stump. The stage is usually in an area with a relatively unobstructed view for 50 feet or more, so sneaking predators can be spotted. Thus, a good drumming site is hard to find and once a male grouse locates one, he tends to use it for life – that is, about three or four years.

Mating, the reason for all this sound and fury, takes place in a matter of seconds after a brief courtship in which the male struts and fans out his tail and neck ruff. The female then disappears back into the thickets, shouldering the perilous task of incubating the eggs on the ground and raising the brood alone. If you see a female grouse trailing her wing as if injured in the coming months, she's bravely trying to lure you away from her chicks.

The male continues to drum for several weeks to attract more females and mate with them. In autumn, he drums again, this time to defend his territory from dispersing males.

To encourage grouse, encourage aspen. Dense expanses of aspen saplings are preferred cover for grouse broods, while stands of poles eight to ten inches in diameter are perfect cover for drumming males. Mature aspens provide buds and catkins, a critical winter food of grouse. To keep up the supply of aspen, a short-lived pioneer species, forests need a regime of periodic disturbance. Forest fires, windstorms, and chainsaws can create ideal grouse habitat.

# may

## first week

May Day is the midpoint between the Spring Equinox and the Summer Solstice.

The chipmunks now being born each weigh about 3.4 grams. They'll be weaned at roughly 50 grams, in just over five weeks.

Wild ginger is flowering. Small pollinating gnats and flies warm themselves within the ground-hugging flower.

Eastern tent caterpillar eggs begin to hatch. These early-season defoliators of hedgerow apple and cherry will soon begin building their unsightly tents.

## second week

The tiny four-petalled flowers of bluets, though only a couple inches high, are sometimes numerous enough to turn a large area a beautiful pale blue.

At this time of year, Baltimore orioles will eat oranges and grape jelly from the bird feeder.

Balsam fir trees are the first conifers to open their buds and show bright, light green needles.

Robins are plucking earthworms to feed their young. When they don't have small mouths to feed, they eat more fruit.

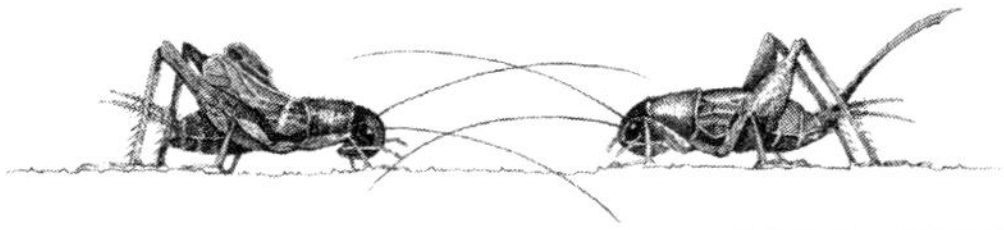



# third week

The clear, musical chirps and trills of the spring field cricket (*Gryllus veletis*) can now be heard.

Wild strawberries flowers provide nectar for many species of bees; mice, deer, chipmunks, and grouse are among the many animals that eat the leaves – not to mention the berries.

Common yellowthroat females are building nests, often within the protective prickles of blackberry thickets.

A single brown thrasher may have 2,000 songs in his repertoire.

# fourth week

White admiral butterflies are as likely to be seen sipping from scat, guano, or puddles as from flowers. The under sides of the wings of white admirals are as pretty as the upper sides. These butterflies are often seen in the forest.

Canada mayflower, also called wild lily of the valley, is blooming.

Moose are giving birth. Usually one calf is produced, though females older than four often have twins. They'll each weigh 300-400 pounds by the fall.

# Turtles Coming Up For a Breath of Fresh Air

BILL AMOS

With April turning to May, northern New England's turtles are getting ready for the summer ahead as they begin to appear at the surface of ponds. After spending the long winter hibernating in bottom mud, they are slow to awaken. That is just as well for the moment, because many species are primarily vegetarian, and pond plants are just beginning to grow. The carnivorous snapping turtle and eat-anything musk turtle may be finding early nourishment, but most of the others must wait – though I have seen plant-eating species snack on worms and soft-bodied insects when an opportunity presented itself.

Of the seven turtle species residing in Vermont and New Hampshire, only two are safely established: the snapping turtle and the eastern painted turtle. When it comes to this part of northern New England, the other five are considered threatened or endangered.

As northerners, our turtles must contend with frigid winters. Unable to maintain the necessary body temperature to carry out essential metabolic activities, a turtle has a heart rate that slows to almost nothing, and its organ systems more or less shut down. Finding food in winter is clearly impossible, so the only source of energy for maintaining minimal metabolism is rich body fat that was stored in the previous summer season of plenty.

Survival is furthermore threatened when turtles' freshwater pond habitat freezes over. An icy ceiling overhead means an end to breathing air at the surface, and the only place to go is to the bottom of the pond for a long winter's sleep. Hibernating turtles don't move or breathe, but they do need a minimal amount of energy to remain alive. Somehow that stored fat has to be metabolized over an extended time, but without oxygen freely available, what to do? The pond turtle's answer is unmatched in degree by any other animal. Modifications to its hibernating lifestyle allow it to survive four or five months without breathing.

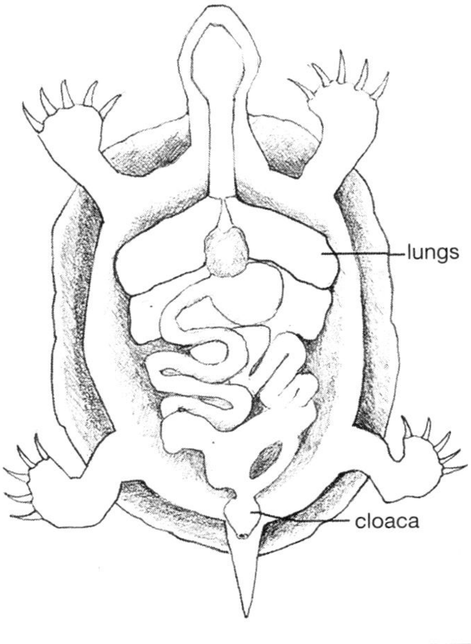

One problem with metabolizing fat in the absence of oxygen is that the process creates lactic acid, and when too much of this acid builds up and results in a condition known as acidosis, it can be fatal to an animal. How to prevent this?

A pond turtle finds a remedy in its shell and skeleton, which together account for over a third of the animal's weight. The shell of a turtle is not just for protection – being heavy it also helps with buoyancy control by counteracting the air-filled lungs, and it acts as a hydrofoil when the animal swims.

For hibernating turtles the shell also is vitally important in a chemical sense. Just as we take buffering tablets, like Tums, to relieve an acid stomach, a hibernating turtle uses its shell and bone, composed of limy compounds, to release carbonates into its increasingly acidic body fluids. This buffers the acid build-up in a non-breathing turtle while it snoozes down in the oxygen-less mud of a winter pond. Deadly acidosis in the animal's tissues is prevented. Furthermore, the shell stores accumulations of this buffered lactic acid where it can do no harm. So a turtle could not survive were it not for the shell's contributions.

In effect, a hibernating turtle is a closed system independent of the environment, an extraordinary feat of biochemical juggling that allows metabolism to continue throughout winter.

But wait. There's more.

All reptiles (also amphibians and birds) have a sizeable rear opening called a cloaca. It is a common, muscular chamber into which the rectum, urinary, and reproductive systems empty. It serves as a mating and egg-laying opening, as well as one through which urinary and digestive wastes escape into the surrounding water. It's a good design that has served these animals well for millions of years.

The cloacas of some kinds of freshwater turtles, such as our eastern painted turtle, have fingerlike extensions that are abundantly supplied with blood vessels. The muscular walls of the cloaca contract and relax, forcing water in and out of the chamber. If a painted turtle hibernates in a pond where some dissolved oxygen is available, the cloaca will serve as a respiratory device. As a substitute "lung," the cloaca allows for the transfer of oxygen and carbon dioxide between the animal and the surrounding water.

Only certain turtles have this ability, but those that do are able to carry on oxygen-fueled metabolism under low-oxygen conditions. The world champion is an Australian river turtle that breathes through its rear end almost all the time. It's a "bum breather," as the Aussies say.

# Giant Silk Moths – Survival of the Fattest

STEVEN D. FACCIO

Many years ago, a friend and fellow naturalist encouraged me to raise cecropia moths as a way of increasing the local population, which had become scarce around my home in southern Connecticut. The decline of the cecropia moth – one of the largest of our native giant silk moths – was linked, ironically, to biological controls that humans were using to kill gypsy moths, exotic moths that were introduced to the U.S. by commercial silk producers. One June afternoon, my friend showed up with a small twig from a black cherry tree. On the underside of one of the leaves were 12 tiny eggs, which, about a week later, hatched into small, black fuzzy caterpillars, no bigger than a grain of rice. My job was to keep them supplied with fresh black cherry leaves.

Within a few weeks, the caterpillars (eating and pooping machines, really) had become green with yellow and blue knobs, and – having grown exponentially – were about the size of my index finger. I marveled at their consumption rate, as the cherry leaves needed replenishing two or three times a day, even though only four or five caterpillars remained. Finally, with only the three largest caterpillars surviving, they pupated into robust, fuzzy cocoons, prompting me to wonder if Darwin had it slightly wrong: survival of the *fattest* might have been more accurate.

There are about 20 species of giant silk moths in North America, but only four species occur in Vermont and New Hampshire. As adults, these are impressive moths indeed. Not only are they enormous – cecropia and polyphemus moths can be as large as your hand – they are also beautiful to look at, with intricate patterns, rich colors, and striking eyespots. Perhaps the best-known *Saturniinae* is the dramatic, lime-green luna moth, with its purple-edged wings, four transparent eyespots, and long curving tails, reminiscent of a barn swallow.

After overwintering in their silken cocoons, adult silk moths typically emerge in June or July. So, beginning in late-May, I checked my three pupae each morning for signs of metamorphosis. Finally, one morning I was rewarded with two fresh moths (both females), their pristine wings completely engorged and dry, while the third (a male) was just beginning to "pump up" its wings. For a cecropia moth "farmer," this is when the fun begins.

If giant silk moth caterpillars are eating and pooping machines, adults are breeding machines. Having only rudimentary mouth parts, they don't feed at all during their short lives, but instead devote all of their energy to locating a mate and reproducing (with only a week or so to live, there's no time to waste). So that evening, I took the newly emerged female moths (identified by their small antennae), placed them in a crudely made wire mesh cage about the size of a microwave oven, and hung it from a cherry tree as a lure. I was fishing for wild cecropias. Meanwhile, the male (identified by his large, feathery antenna) would have to wait before being released.

After emergence, female giant silk moths remain physically inactive, conserving their limited fat reserves while minimizing exposure to predators. Nevertheless, they communicate chemically with males, letting them know where they are. Using a gland on the tip of their abdomens, females release a plume of pheromones into the evening air. This "perfume" is detected by the males' highly branched, feathery antennae, which contain tiny, hair-like structures called sensilla. Receptor cells on the sensilla bind with the pheromone molecules, stimulating the males to relentlessly follow the scent trail. Although the distance from which males can detect the pheromone is still unknown, marked individuals have been recovered up to 20 miles away in just a few days' time.

After just one night of it hanging in the cherry tree, I was surprised to find a male cecropia on the outside of the cage the following morning. His wings were pale and tattered, evidence of his efforts to locate a female, with which he was now abdomen-to-abdomen through the wire mesh. Another tattered male was present the following day after I had released the captive male (so he could join the breeding population that was evidently in the area). The two captive females laid dozens of eggs each, only to die shortly thereafter, having accomplished their sole purpose in life.

I continued to raise cecropia moths for a couple years, releasing maybe a dozen individuals to the surrounding area. Whether or not I was actually helping out the local population was unclear, but since my female "lures" never had any trouble attracting wild male moths, I eventually decided that, in the grand scheme of things, I was probably having very little impact. Despite my good intentions, it appeared that survival of the fittest (or fattest) was working quite well without my help.

# Sneaky Plants and Gullible Ants

Howard Krum

I don't trust flowers.

There are grounds for my suspicion; flowering plants are proven masters of deception. For instance, the sundew uses sparkling droplets of sticky "faux dew" to ensnare and digest curious flies; bee orchids dupe male wasps into wasting their copulatory efforts on floral structures that look and smell like female wasps. And what about humans? As I labor on behalf of flowers, fertilizing, tilling, watering, and sweating, I sometimes wonder if I'm being led down the proverbial garden path. *Exactly who's cultivating whom?*

Flowering plants have many strategies for disseminating their progeny. Some dispersal methods are straightforward: maple keys helicopter hundreds of yards, springy jewelweed pods eject their spawn, and tiny willow seeds float miles on watery currents. Many, like the burdock, hitch rides on animals (as my grandfather used to say, "burdock-burdock, he's your friend, he'll stick with you 'til the end."). I can even respect the lowly dandelion with its swarm of germinal fuzz and naked ambition for earthly domination – at least it's honest.

But others, the shiftier of the lot, are not below a trick or two. I recently spoke with Dr. Elizabeth Farnsworth (co-author of *A Field Guide to the Ants of New England*) and it turns out that loads of spring perennials employ an interesting scheme called myrmecochory. They use ants to spread their offspring. Species including the bloodroot (*Sanguinaria canadensis*), dutchman's breeches (*Dicentra cucullaria*), and various violets grow extra-tough seeds capped with fleshy appendages called elaiosomes. These structures, packed with ant-edible lipids, proteins, carbohydrates, and vitamins, are also laced with oleic acid – a pheromone that is present in insect corpses and has been shown to attract carnivorous ants.

What usually happens is that ants are drawn to the ripening seeds, then lug them back to (and often into) their burrowed nests. There, in the relative safety of the colony, the ants feed the elaiosomes to their maturing larvae and discard the seeds.

For decades, this relationship has been touted as a fine example of interspecies quid pro quo. In comparison to the plant-insect interaction of the sundew, the relationship a local trillium patch has with a neighboring *Aphaenogaster* colony seems downright quaint. The ant gets a snack. The plant benefits from seed transport away from the parent (and thereby reduced competition between seedlings) to sites that are protected from predators and often feature ideal substrates for germination.

Seed dispersal by ants is a worldwide phenomenon involving more than 11,000 plant species (4.5 percent of all plants) across multiple ecosystems. In fact, myrmecochory is a key evolutionary driver for flowering plant diversity. Ant-dispersed lineages in 241 genera from all continents except Antarctica contain on average more than twice as many species as do their non-myrmecochorous kin. But scientists are starting to wonder if this ain't a lopsided deal for the ant.

Recent studies have shown that even though ants can digest elaiosome nutrients, the benefit to the ant colony is questionable – or, at least, highly variable. Colony success can be measured in pupae production (number and mass) and sex ratio (queens versus workers). In several experiments, sexual production, allocation, and weight did not differ significantly between elaiosome-supplemented and unsupplemented diets. In other experiments, ants preferred oleic acid-laden seed that actually *reduced* reproductive output.

On a recent spring day, after clearing more space for hollyhocks, I was snapped out of my horticultural complacency when our mailman delivered the tenth in a series of unsolicited seed catalogs. There, printed on the pulpy backs of their cousin trees was one glossy, floral display after another – flowering plants shamelessly luring me to buy, ship, and sow their offspring. When I finally pulled my nose from the enticing pages I noticed, as if for the first time, that flowering greenery had completely surrounded our home. I dropped the seed rag where I stood, slack-jawed. The flowers had played me like an ant.

For a fun spring activity related to this essay, turn to page 200.

# Arms Race in the Woods: How Beavers Recycle Tree Defenses

DIETLAND MÜLLER-SCHWARZE

Around a beaver pond, we sometimes catch a whiff of beaver odor. People have described it to me as smoky, woody, or like tobacco. It may waft over from the lodge, or it might emanate from scent mounds – little piles of mud by the water's edge. Beavers make scent mounds by dredging up mud from the bottom of a pond, then carrying it up on land in their front paws while walking upright. The beaver drops the mud, then squats over the mound and applies castoreum from glands near the base of the tail.

The smell means: keep away! In some neighborhoods, this territorial advertisement works remarkably well. I've been involved in studies where human-made scent mounds effectively deterred free-ranging beavers from settling in unoccupied beaver habitat.

When a beaver detects a foreign castor smell in its territory, it implies brazen behavior that has to be dealt with. The residents invariably eliminate the strange scent mark. They paw it apart and scent mark over it. If they come across the perpetrator, they'll attack viciously. Researchers have found that beavers can identify family members by their castor smell; they can also distinguish between neighbors and complete strangers.

Castoreum contains many different kinds of compounds: alkaloids, phenolics, terpenes, alcohols, and acids among them. The beaver appropriates the ingredients from the plants it eats; ironically, the plants use the compounds to say: keep away!

Plants synthesize a bewildering variety of secondary compounds that differ from the basic classes of proteins, fats, and carbohydrates. Some, like alkaloids, taste bitter, while tannins are astringent. When they work, the compounds defend the plants against mammal and insect herbivores, as well as fungi and other microorganisms. These secondary compounds interfere with digestion and inhibit reproduction. Some are outright toxic and even deadly.

Compounds from a number of trees in the beaver's diet end up in their castoreum. Benzyl alcohol occurs in aspens and poplars, benzoic acid in black cherry and scots pine, and catechol in common cottonwood. In summer, beavers eat aquatic plants such as pondweed and pond lilies – the alkaloids that these plants use to deter insects also end up in the beaver's mix.

Beavers cope with plant chemicals in different ways. They have in their saliva a protein that binds tannins and renders them harmless. They deal with other compounds by breaking them down into their component parts: when they ingest salicin – a bitter chemical in willow and poplar bark – the salicin molecule gets broken down into sugar and, eventually, salicylic acid. (Beavers are not the only animals that perform this trick – leaf beetles also ingest salicin when munching on willow leaves. They use the glucose as a nutrient and the salicylic acid for defense against predators, such as ants.)

Even humans appropriate beaver castor, though we use it to say: come here! Castor sacs are a secondary product of the fur trade and are sold to perfumers who use the castor to give perfumes an "animal note." In fact, the chemical investigation of castoreum was driven by the perfume industry.

We're also not above recycling plant compounds for our own purposes. Salicylic acid is the active principle of aspirin. Over 2,000 years ago, physicians in ancient Greece prescribed willow bark to fight fevers and inflammation. Native Americans used willow bark against headaches, and today we still treat pain of the lower back and osteoarthritis with willow bark preparations.

And so there rages a chemical arms race in the woods. Trees bolster their defenses against herbivores, especially during the dormant season. Beavers and other animals defeat these defenses by breaking down, detoxing, sequestering, and recycling potentially harmful compounds. Plotting their next move, trees will crank up their defenses. Two- and three-year-old aspen saplings are rich in bitter-tasting, salicin-like glycosides. Beavers avoid these and feed on larger, less bitter trees, allowing the young trees to prevail. The race goes on and no one ever wins. Each measure provokes a countermeasure.

# Dandelions: Make Salad, Not War with Lawn Invaders

JOE RANKIN

There's no arguing spring with the dandelions. When they bloom, I know that winter's finally outta here. By May, my fields and yard are dusted with that mellow dandelion yellow. I don't mind. I keep honeybees, and dandelions are one of the more reliable sources of early spring nectar and pollen.

Dandelion is a poetic name. Derived from the French phrase *dent de leon*, it refers to the deep serrations of the leaves, which, at least to the French, resemble the teeth (dent) of a lion (leon). The flower heads are packed with innumerable tiny florets. The heads open during the day and close at night.

Arthur Haines, the research botanist for the New England Wild Flower Society, explained that there are only a handful of dandelion species in the Northeast. The large-lobed dandelion, *Taraxacum latilobum*, is a North American native that Haines described as "exceedingly rare." The red-seeded dandelion, *Taraxacum laevigatum*, a European import, is also uncommon. Hawkweeds and hawkbits, which bloom in the late summer and fall, are look-alikes but not true dandelions.

So, this time of year, when you gaze across a yellow sea of fuzzy flower heads, chances are you're looking at *Taraxacum officinale*. This is the common dandelion, a native of Eurasia that has spread its weedy presence around the globe, helped along by another weedy species – humans.

Many credit – or blame – the Pilgrims for bringing dandelions to the New World. That may be true, or not. The plants also could have come as seeds in the hooves of livestock, or in imported hay, or in a dozen other ways. Once they got here, they spread like a yellow flame.

"It has been really successful, like the common plantain. They're all weeds and weeds are simply adapted to reseeding disturbed habitat," Haines told me. "Dandelions need access to mineral soil and disturbed soil. Those plants are doing well now because humans have so disturbed the environment." He noted that dandelions don't really compete with native species or invade pristine ecosystems. Instead, they typically crowd out other non-native plants. Like...grass.

From a dandelion's point of view, a beautiful green lawn is nothing but a disturbed habitat just waiting for it to sink its taproot. From a lawn fetishist's point of view, dandelions are Public Enemy No. 1. By some estimates, Americans douse their lawns with 90 million pounds of chemicals a year. Most of those are herbicides and, you can bet your little yellow flowers, most are aimed directly at dandelions. It's not only an expensive battle, it's a foolish one, as people are poisoning the environment in a war they can't win.

You could take a different view of the dandelion. It's a view that goes back millennia, to our foraging ancestors who saw *T. officinale* as an herbal medicine and valuable food source. They're good steamed, sautéed, or simply blanched in hot water and drained. Dandelion leaves make a healthful salad (the best time to harvest them is early spring, before a plant blooms). Yellow flower heads can be used to make wine. The taproot can be harvested for food or to make a coffee-like beverage. The dandelion's value on the menu is evidenced by the fact that plant breeders have developed cultivars with bigger leaves, and others that are self-blanching to take out the bitterness.

"The dandelion is extremely beneficial to human health," enthused Haines. He noted that their leaves contain large amounts of carotene, which is converted by the body to vitamin A. The plants have essential minerals including calcium and manganese. They contain lecithin, an emulsifier that helps keep fat in solution and so helps the body absorb more fat-soluble vitamins. The list of the dandelion's healthful constituents is long. "It is amazingly beneficial," Haines said. Instead of grubbing up dandelions, he advised, "we should be eating them all spring and gathering the taproots all summer."

And dandelions don't just have value as a health food. Children, and the occasional adult, find tremendous joy in blowing fluffy dandelion seed heads into the wind. Blowing off all the seed heads is purported to make wishes come true – exactly as often as blowing out a birthday candle. And dandelions are accomplished muses, proliferating like, well, dandelions, across a variety of different art forms and genres, from Walt Whitman to The Rolling Stones.

So, let's sing the dandelion's praises, whether at a poetry slam or in a salad bowl. Then blow off the seed heads and make a wish...but not for a perfect green lawn.

For a fun spring activity related to this essay, turn to page 198.

# Amphibian Skin: Toxic Chemicals to Medical Marvels

By Steven D. Faccio

I was eating breakfast when I noticed a black duck quietly feeding on our small pond. It would occasionally "tip-up" – head underwater, tail skyward – in typical puddle duck fashion. Suddenly, the peaceful scene was interrupted as the duck began spinning wildly in circles, one wing flapping frantically as water splashed in all directions. Ten seconds later and just as suddenly, all was calm, including the duck, which was now floating belly-up. I searched for signs of an underwater predator, perhaps an otter or the Loch Ness Monster, but saw nothing. A little shocked, I carefully fished the duck out and brought it to the office where a colleague and I conducted a quick necropsy. Not really expecting any answers, we were quite surprised when we opened the gizzard and found it stuffed with at least a dozen undigested adult eastern newts. I was aware that newt skin contained toxins, but wondered if it was potent enough to kill a three-pound duck so quickly.

At first glance, amphibians appear rather defenseless. Most are quite small, move relatively slowly, lack any protective armor or claws, and have tiny teeth that are incapable of providing meaningful defense. However, all amphibians have glands that, in addition to keeping their skin moist and improving respiration, also cause them to be slippery. While this in itself can aid in defense, they also have glands that produce toxic secretions, the potency of which is highly variable, ranging from distasteful, to a mild irritant, to deadly. In the case of the eastern newt (as well as all North American newts), it's deadly.

Newts contain a powerful poison called *tarichatoxin*, which is biochemically very similar to *tetrodotoxin*, or TTX, found in pufferfish. A highly potent neurotoxin, TTX is the most poisonous non-protein substance known to science. Once it enters the bloodstream, TTX acts quickly by blocking the conduction of nerve signals to the muscles, causing blood vessels to relax, leading to a sudden drop in blood pressure. Basically, the toxin blocks the signals from your brain that tell your heart to beat and your lungs to breathe. There have been several cases of human poisoning from newts, including at least one death, but ordinary handling is not dangerous, as the poison must enter the digestive tract or the bloodstream. The bright orange, immature, terrestrial stage of the eastern newt, known as the red eft, contains 10 times as much TTX as the drab-colored adults.

In many cases, it's not the potency of the toxic secretion, but the stickiness or disagreeable taste that provides the amphibian with an opportunity to escape a potential predator. In many salamanders, including the spotted and Jefferson salamanders, poison glands are concentrated in the tail. When a predator is encountered, salamanders assume a defensive posture, often elevating or "waggling" their tail toward the attacker, while a sticky, whitish substance is secreted. If the predator "takes the bait" and gets a mouthful of noxious salamander "goo," it often decides to seek more palatable prey elsewhere.

In most of our local frog species, including the American bullfrog, green, mink, and wood frogs, poison glands are uniformly distributed over the entire skin surface. While the toxicity of the secretions is relatively mild in these species, it is apparently distasteful to some mammals and birds.

Toads in the genus *Bufo*, on the other hand, including the widespread American toad, have poison glands concentrated in "warts" on their backs, and in two large paratoid glands behind their eyes. When grabbed by a predator (including dogs and cats), the paratoid glands release a whitish, foamy secretion consisting of three substances: *bufogenin* and *bufotoxin* – which affect the adrenal and cardiovascular systems – and *bufotenin*, an alkaloid which is a powerful hallucinogen also found in some mushrooms. In most cases, the toad is quickly released due to the repulsive taste of the toxins. Then, for the next several hours, as a lingering reminder of the encounter, the predator is left with a variety of symptoms – including salivation, nausea, vomiting, heart arrhythmia, and hallucinations. If an entire toad is ingested, the symptoms range from convulsive seizures, to paralysis, neurological disorders, and even death.

Amphibian secretions are not all bad, however. More than 200 chemical toxins considered to be beneficial in medical research have been isolated from just a small percentage of the world's amphibian species. One alkaloid produced by a tropical poison dart frog is a highly effective painkiller, 200 times stronger than morphine without being addictive. Skin secretions from the Australian green treefrog stimulate activity in the human pancreas and intestine, and commercial drugs are now available based on these compounds. Some amphibian skin secretions, like those of the African clawed frog, also have powerful antibiotic properties that help heal cuts and bruises, which may provide doctors with a whole new class of antibiotics in the years ahead.

# june

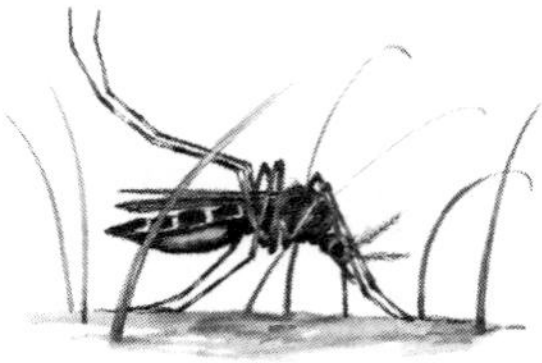



# 1 first week

On fine mornings, honey bees may swarm, leaving the hive with the old queen.
A new queen will emerge from the old hive and mate with several drones high in the air.

The Virginia ctenuchid is a day-flying moth.
Its feathery antennae, orange-marked head, iridescent blue body,
and brown wings make it easy to identify.

The lavender and white flowers of showy orchis
are being pollinated by insects with long tongues:
some bumblebees, butterflies, and moths.

# 2 second week

The yellow dust that's particularly noticeable on cars and still bodies of water
is probably white pine pollen. It's produced in abundance at this time of year.

Human exhalations have four to five percent more carbon dioxide
than the surrounding air and mosquitos use this difference,
as well as their heat detection system, to find us –
sometimes from more than 100 yards away.

Blackflies are among the many insects
that are pollinating blueberry flowers.

# third week

Bobolinks will soon fledge from nests in fields that have not been mowed. Listen for the effervescent song of the male as he flies up from the grasses.

Loon eggs, usually two of them, are hatching. Both parents have shared incubation duties during the past 28 days.

Phoebe chicks are leaving the nest. Soon the backdoor (or barn door, or...) can be used again.

Bullfrogs are calling from the cover of vegetation at the edges of still or slow-moving water.

# fourth week

Grouse chicks can fly, but they don't fly very well.

Male gray tree frogs are calling, mostly at night. They make a racket but tend to go to bed soon after midnight.

Gray fox pups that were born in March or April are now learning to hunt. They might be climbing trees to escape predators or to catch squirrels.

American goldfinches begin building nests. They form pairs in May but delay brood rearing till the seeds of thistles and other composites are ripe.

# For Uncommon Beauty, Nothing Beats the Orchid

CHARLES W. JOHNSON

One of the pleasures of the brief northern spring is moseying about in back forties to learn what birds are arriving, what insects are emerging, and what flowers are blooming. And among the most rewarding finds this time of year are the always-uncommon, sometimes-very-rare wild orchids. These exquisite yet bizarre flowers are members of one of the largest and most widespread groups of plants on earth. The orchid family has 15,000 to 30,000 species, 5 to 10 percent of all species of flowering plants, yet, paradoxically, that family includes some of the rarest plants in North America.

While most orchids are tropical and epiphytic (growing on trees), the 200 or so species in temperate North America are largely terrestrial; some are strictly boreal in distribution. In northern New England, most native orchids are uncommon, at the very least, while many are labeled threatened or endangered. Their status is tenuous largely because the habitats in which they live are themselves rare. In the Northeast, for example, more than half of the 60 known species are restricted to peatlands (acidic bogs and more-neutral fens).

The most common orchid species in northern New England – though never common in the sense of dandelions or maples – is the moccasin flower, with its pink or white "lady's-slipper" blossom. It prefers acidic softwoods, while other forest-dwelling species, such as the rattlesnake plantains and showy orchis, are the less dramatic, less seen dwellers of mixed forests. In the special, restricted landscapes of peatlands, white bog orchid is a regular inhabitant, while grass pink, rose pogonia, dragon's mouth, and showy lady's slipper – all with pink or reddish blossoms – are significantly rarer, growing almost exclusively in open, less-acidic fens. Several species are imperiled by even more restricted habitats, such as the delicate fairy-slipper of a few northern cedar swamps, ram's-head lady's slipper in certain limestone-rich locales, and the small whorled pogonia that grows in just a few acidic woodlands. For flower lovers, the sight of these orchids often etches into permanent memory.

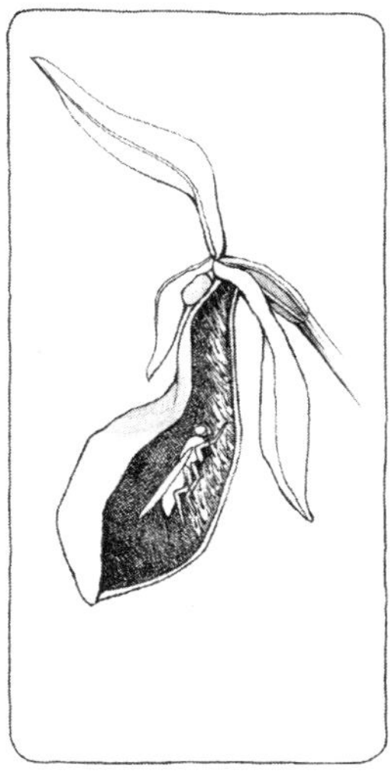

With their highly evolved flowers, nearly all orchids are utterly dependent on insects for their perpetuation. Unlike many other groups of flowering plants, in orchids the pollen is clumped in a sticky wad – known as a pollinium – that is locked or hidden deep within the flower where winds cannot bear it away and most insects cannot reach it. The pollinium can be removed only by adhering to a specific pollinator, usually an insect, thereby hitching a ride to another flower. The showy, colorful, and often strongly scented blossom attracts the appropriate type of species, one that is able to navigate the flower's unique anatomy and affect pollination. In many tropical species, the deception and trapping is elaborate; some flowers even mimic the female insect, luring the male into false anticipation of copulation!

Our native New England orchids, while not to this extreme, have their own ways of luring, deceiving, and entrapping insects. In the moccasin flower, for example, a bee enters through a slit in the "slipper," likely drawn to the fragrance of the hairs lining the inside. Finding no nectar there, the bee leaves, not by the slit (which is not visible from the inside) but through an opening at the top where it rubs against the pollinium. The pollinium sticks to the bee and is carried to a new flower, where cross-pollination occurs.

The grass pink has other trickery. Here, the flower's big lip projects straight up, is hinged at the base, and has many stamen-like filaments. But the flower has neither stamens nor nectar, and when the duped visitor – usually a bee of the right size and weight – lands on the lip in anticipation of reward, the lip folds inward at the hinge and the bee drops upside down onto the pollinium. The bee struggles out, the pollinium sticking to its back, flies to another flower and repeats the procedure, transferring the pollinium in the process.

Later in the summer, orchid seeds are numerous – often thousands per flower – and they are tiny and light enough to become windborne like pollen. The seeds are so small mainly because they lack endosperm, the food normally stored for the developing embryo. Instead, the poorly organized orchid embryo obtains its food from a fungus that invades each seed, an association that continues in the adult orchid, with the fungus growing and taking up residence in the roots.

Probably due to their inextricable tie to these fungi, as well as their dependence on such specific habitats, orchids are notoriously sensitive about their living conditions, and unpredictable bloomers even when growing in what seem to be the most suitable of places. They may be prolific one year but the next not a flower is to be found. Or they may suddenly reappear where they have been absent for decades. But most troubling is their outright loss, either due to destruction of their habitats or plundering by collectors for their beauty, delicacy, and rarity.

See one, and consider yourself blessed.

# The Tree Fox

MEGHAN McCARTHY McPHAUL

When you think of foxes (if you ever do), you likely picture the ginger-coated red fox, like Mr. Tod from Beatrix Potter's fantastical children's tales, only without the dapper suitcoat and tweed knickers. It is the less common gray fox, however, that has been wandering the woods and fields near my home – and climbing the trees.

That's right: gray foxes can climb trees, a distinction they share with only one other member of the Canidae family, the raccoon dog of East Asia. This arboreal ability provides several benefits for the gray fox, from evading predators to reaching food.

It was this fondness for trees that led me to our neighborhood gray fox last winter. Curious about the jumbled network of dainty tracks surrounding an old apple tree just beyond the back vegetable garden, I set the game camera at the base of its trunk. Just like that, I had a dozen nighttime images of a beautiful gray fox, black lines running like streaked mascara from its eyes, thick ruff of fur around its neck, and an enormously bushy tail, topped and tipped in black.

That ridge of black guard hairs along the tail, and the black tip, are features that definitively revealed this fox as a gray, not a red. Gray foxes have coarser hair than reds, although their mostly black-and-gray coat is dappled with rusty red. They are also stockier than their red counterparts, with shorter legs.

Although similar in size and sharing some habits of red foxes, gray foxes represent an entirely separate branch of Canidae evolution and are in the genus Urocyon (rather than Vulpes, the genus that comprises red and many other foxes). The gray fox's ancestors separated from other canid species 3.6 million years ago, and *Urocyon cinereoargenteus*, the gray fox, is considered among the oldest species in the Canidae family.

Gray foxes did not exist in many parts of northern New England, at least in recent history, but furbearer harvest records in both New Hampshire and Vermont indicate that they're expanding their range. "The last 10 years, there are some records of gray foxes being trapped in Coös County [New Hampshire's most northern county], which is not historically a stronghold for them," said Eric Orff, a wildlife biologist and retired long-time furbearer biologist for the New Hampshire Fish and Game Department. "It's an animal that's on the move. They're seeking new territory, moving north."

This shift could be partly due to habitat availability. While red foxes prefer open fields, gray foxes do well with a mixture of forest and old fields bordered by brushy edges. That perfectly describes the setting beyond our yard – and in much of northern New England, where farmland has reverted back to forest.

The gray fox's curved, semi-retractable claws and flexible front legs may also give the animal a literal leg up over their red fox brethren in the region. Unlike red foxes, grays are able to evade coyotes by climbing trees – they sometimes even den in tree hollows far above the ground. Their arboreal skills also enable them to reach fruit that red foxes can't.

Gray foxes mate once a year, in late winter. The mating pair share responsibility for raising offspring, and the family generally stays together until fall.

While the kits – normally three to five in a litter – are confined to the den, the male fox (known as a tod), goes out hunting while the vixen remains with the kits. By June, the kits are weaned – and hungry. With so many mouths to fill, the parent foxes, mostly nocturnal, are more likely to venture out on hunting excursions during daylight hours. And that leads to a surge of calls to fish and game departments from people concerned about spotting the normally secretive foxes, said Orff. "June is the fox month."

June may be "fox month" for wildlife officers, but all traces of my neighborhood gray foxes have disappeared by this time of year: without tracks pressed into snow, I don't know much about their wanderings.

Some of the game camera images from late in the winter show two foxes together. Perhaps that means there is a den nearby, and gray fox pups will soon be out with their parents learning to hunt. I hope that next winter, I'll find more fox tracks around the old apple tree.

# Ground Beetles: In a Pitfall Can Near You

VIRGINIA BARLOW

Some ground beetles are big and beautiful: shiny black or iridescent green or bluish. And because many of them are unable or reluctant to fly, they are easily caught; you can get a good long look at them as they wiggle to escape from your hand. They are members of the family Carabidae, and the common name, ground beetle, describes them well. That is where you will find them, especially the forest species – hiding under rocks and logs during the day, waiting for a night of feasting, mostly on live prey.

Good predators that they are, they disappear instantly when their log or rock is picked up, for most of them have strong legs. That's about as much generalizing as you can do with this family of around 40,000 described species – perhaps the largest of all insect families – with 1,700 species in North America. A few, such as the snail-eating carabids, have very restricted diets and are shaped accordingly. An elongated head and hooked mandibles allow these beetles to reach deep into a snail shell and grasp the soft and luckless inhabitant. Ross Bell, an entomologist at the University of Vermont, told me that some snail-eaters follow rodent burrows in pursuit of their prey and mimic the sound of a rattlesnake to intimidate any mice in residence.

Many ground beetles emit toxic secretions to fend off predators, an art perfected almost beyond belief by the group called bombardier beetles. Some people believe that the bombardiers' elaborate mechanism for shooting blasts of boiling toxic chemicals out the back end cannot have come about through evolution. You have to admit, they have an argument, but one that has been countered, needless to say. Bell said that it is not difficult to find these mythical beetles right here in New England, and that anybody who looks in the right place can experience the popping sound of their explosions and see the tiny puffs of smoke.

Over millions of years, this successful family has conservatively held on to a simple body plan. A few sand-dwelling species are tiny and round with small legs, but most look like ordinary beetles. A few species consume seeds, and a few eat only one particular kind of insect, but most are not at all fussy about what they eat. Instead, they are picky, often extremely picky, about their habitat and often prefer to live within a very narrow temperature, humidity, light intensity, and/or pH range – plus they may be sensitive to other factors that we aren't even aware of. Some protect their eggs with a coating of clay, and if kept in peat they refuse to lay eggs.

Ground beetles have a simple social life, which makes them easier to study than ants or bees. As an added bonus, they don't sting. At night you can catch large numbers of ground beetles in pitfall traps. In the simplest case, this is just a coffee can buried up to its rim in the ground.

Diverse, abundant, food generalists, habitat specialists, easy to feed, and easily caught: it all adds up to a ready-made ecological monitoring system and, indeed, that is what they are being used for nowadays. Trees, being very long-lived, are almost useless as ecological indicators. You have to do something terrible to a tree species before it disappears, but the composition and abundance of the insect community fluctuates at least annually, and conclusions can be drawn from careful monitoring of insect populations.

In Europe, ground beetles have been studied intensively, but in this country, efforts to correlate beetle populations with environmental change are at an early stage. Both the number of ground beetle species and the number of a particular species can indicate environmental changes. Within a small area, changes in the plant community will result in a very different assortment of ground beetles at the bottom of your pitfall trap.

Most forest species are almost never found in fields and, as a group, they tend to be nocturnal and flightless, preferring moist, cool conditions.

Are they pests? Are they beneficial? Tree-climbing ground beetles in the genus Calosoma may be important predators on lepidopteran caterpillars, especially the saddled prominent. Other ground beetles eat earthworms. Several large Carabus species were brought here from Europe to control gypsy moths, and some of them have spread across the country, with little effect on gypsy moths, but a big effect on anyone who sees them: they are among the biggest, most iridescent, and most beautiful of all ground beetles.

If you set up a pitfall can, you can get a close look at these beetles and then release them where you found them. If you don't have a field guide that includes beetles, try bugguide.net.

For a fun summer activity related to this essay, turn to page 208.

# An Osprey Takes the Plunge

David Deen

Flyfishing from a canoe in a small headwater pond at the tippity-top of the Connecticut River is usually a quiet experience. That's why the sudden splash caused me to turn my head just in time to see an osprey struggling up out of the water and into the air.

My first thought was that the bird had misjudged its attempt at a fish, splashing down instead of plucking the fish out of the water. The bird quickly flew up about 25 feet above the water and began to half-fly, half-hover in a circle. Before long it made a second, wings-folded, headlong dive downward. But instead of expanding its wings and grasping acrobatically with its talons for a fish, the bird went headfirst into the water.

If you are as ignorant as I was about the fishing techniques of ospreys, you might think this particular bird had a technique problem. I imagined it must have given itself a throbbing headache from smacking into the water at full speed diving for a fish. All for nothing.

Later, I learned that this bird was actually doing what it was supposed to do. The osprey is the only raptor that dives into the water with its feet thrust forward on either side of its head. This allows the bird to keep the fish in sight throughout the dive, and the feet hitting the water first cut through the water's surface and protect the head. Conveniently, the osprey also has closable nostrils to keep water out during impact.

An osprey's feet are specially designed to help them secure fish. Heavy scales and small, needle-sharp spikes (known as spicules) help them hold on to their catch. The outer talons can rotate forward or backward, much like an opposable thumb, allowing the osprey to align a captured fish parallel to its own body for better aerodynamics in flight. All told, an adult osprey can take off with ease if the fish is less than 25 percent of its two- to four-pound body weight.

The osprey I was watching flew up to a branch hanging over the pond and sat patiently, watching the pond like a hawk. Which it almost is: the osprey's taxonomic name, *Pandion haliaetus*, means "sea hawk" in Greek, and the bird is commonly called a "fish hawk." The osprey is not a true hawk but rather the only member of the Pandion family group, found on all continents except Antarctica.

The mouth of the Connecticut River at Long Island Sound contains the highest concentration of breeding ospreys along the southern New England coast. In the early 1940s, there were approximately 200 nesting pairs of ospreys at the mouth of the Connecticut. Populations declined steadily to only a few pairs by the early 1960s, due to exposure to the pesticide DDT. More recent figures, from 2001, show 47 active nesting pairs in the river's lower reaches, a notable rebound.

The osprey population in the upper Connecticut River watershed is likewise still recovering from DDT. Only the northern reaches of the river currently have active nesting sites, and field studies have documented no active nesting attempts in the rest of the Vermont/New Hampshire reach of the river. In New Hampshire during the 2004 nesting season, eight young fledged from five active nests. In Vermont, as of 2007, there were six recorded nesting sites in the upper reach of the river.

Because the use of DDT has been outlawed in the United States, it's easy to think that the threat to ospreys is long gone. But ospreys are long-distance migrants and are exposed to DDT during their migration and in their wintering areas, where the use of DDT is not forbidden. Most of the ospreys found in the Connecticut Valley spend the winter in South America, though a few join the snowbirds in the Florida Keys.

Back on the pond, the osprey's third try was a charm. The bird flew to the center of the pond, suddenly fell out of the sky as though shot, dove straight into the pond head-first and, on reappearing, had a fish tenuously gripped between two talons. It quickly secured the fish with both feet, oriented it straight ahead and, despite the wiggling, held on to the fish and flew off.

I, on the other hand, safe and dry in my canoe, did not land a fish all day.

# The Spittlebug – A Jumping Champ in a Bubble Bath

Li Shen

On the lower levels of the food chain, danger is rarely out of spitting distance. Risk from predators has spurred the evolution of many clever adaptations – camouflage coloring, speedy retreat, distasteful secretions, and armor plating among them. Small jumping insects known as froghoppers approach concealment in a unique way: their developing nymphs cover themselves in a bubble bath. From this trick they derive their common name, "spittlebug."

If you investigate the clumps of white froth, sometimes referred to as "cow spit" or "frog spit," that appear on plant stems this time of year, you'll find that each dollop of foam envelops a soft, greenish insect. Who would have thought that this froth, so soft and insubstantial, could be protective? Yet predators can't see the bug for the bubbles, and if they probe the foam, they soon find that it has an acrid taste. The spittlebug's foam is also a good insulator against heat and cold. And it is a great moisturizer, without which the soft-bodied nymph would soon dry up.

Despite its name, spittlebug "spit" isn't spit at all, but comes from the other end of the bug. Like all insects in the order Hemiptera (true bugs, not to be confused with the common usage of the word "bug" for insect), spittlebugs feed on plant sap through piercing mouthparts. Worldwide, there are a wide variety of spittlebug species.

Spittlebugs suck sap from the xylem, the long tubular cells that transport water in plant stems; most other sucking insects feed on the phloem that lies close beneath a plant's outer sheath. Since the xylem sap contains fewer nutrients than the phloem, the spittlebug has to process a lot of fluid in order to grow.

The bug feeds standing on its head and excretes excess fluid from its anus. This fluid runs down and coats the spittlebug's body. Specialized glands mix in mucilaginous compounds that increase the viscosity of the fluid and also stabilize the bubbles. The nymph sucks air into its abdominal breathing tube and then forces it out to blow bubbles while pumping its abdomen up and down. As bubbles form, it uses its legs to pull the froth over its body. Safe within this foamy bath, the nymph grows and molts a few times, finally emerging as an adult.

The adult spittlebug, or froghopper, is a rather drab, stubby creature in shades of brown to gray. However, it too has a claim to fame. Although it is a fraction of an inch in length (the common meadow spittlebug averages less than a quarter of an inch), this bug can jump more than two feet in the air. This is equivalent to a human leaping over the Gateway Arch in St. Louis. This revelation has established the spittlebug as one of nature's most powerful jumpers.

The froghopper doesn't have enormous hind legs, so how does it do it? The mechanism can best be compared to a crossbow. Large internal muscles stretch an elastic structure composed of a substance dubbed resilin. This appears to be the perfect rubber – it can remain stretched to over twice its length for months, and still rebound to its original dimensions. The stretched resilin exerts tension and flexes the bug's stiff exoskeleton, like flexing a bow. When this tension is released, it powers explosive extension of the rear legs. When not jumping, the bug keeps its rear legs poised for takeoff and only uses its four front legs to walk about.

A jumping froghopper moves 10 times faster than a flea. In fact, the acceleration is so great that the bug is subjected to a force equivalent to 400 times that of gravity. Compare that to a diving fighter plane, which reaches a force equivalent of about 10 g's. That's an impressive feat for a little bug, and another great example of an outstanding adaptation to escape predators.

# Old Logs Take on New Life

BILL AMOS

When a tree nears the end of its life span, woodpeckers may arrive to puncture holes in its trunk. Rainwater running into the openings can carry bacterial and fungal spores that attack cellulose and lignin, and rotting is likely to begin and spread into the heartwood. Carpenter ants, longhorn beetles, and carpenter moth larvae bore into the wood. Bark beetles shoulder their way under the loosening bark, followed by flat centipedes, crustacean woodlice, wood roaches, and tiny mites.

The arrival of such creatures is a sign of a troubled tree, one still standing but probably not for long.

Eventually, the old tree surrenders its hold on life, topples over and lies partly hidden in forest undergrowth. The rotting process that helped fell the tree accelerates after the trunk is on the ground. Woody tissues become softened by capillary water drawn from the soil. More small creatures enter the decaying wood. Labyrinthine galleries are excavated and widened under the bark as one population of organisms after another becomes established, each flourishing before being replaced by successors.

In death, the fallen tree takes on a complex new role as it offers shelter, sustenance, and protected nurseries for myriad creatures and plants. During a visit to one, I lifted sheets of bark and teased apart wood fibers to find millipedes, slugs, snails, bessybugs, and rove beetles. Using a magnifier, I found springtails and pseudoscorpions. Exposed under flaking bark were shiny, yellow slime molds.

Meanwhile, the deteriorating log becomes a focal point for larger visitors: chipmunks, maybe a porcupine, occasionally a grouse. Squirrels may arrive to dismember pinecones atop the trunk, and a gray fox might use the log's unobstructed crest to watch for prey in surrounding vegetation. A black bear arrives to rip off loose bark in a search for succulent grubs.

The smaller organisms of varying species and numbers keep coming. They distribute themselves throughout the log according to the wood's exposure to light and air and its degree of rot and dampness. While many insects and those slime molds avoid light, many plants require it. Green algae take advantage of sunlight where bark has peeled away; mosses and liverworts appear later, and lichens begin their slow growth.

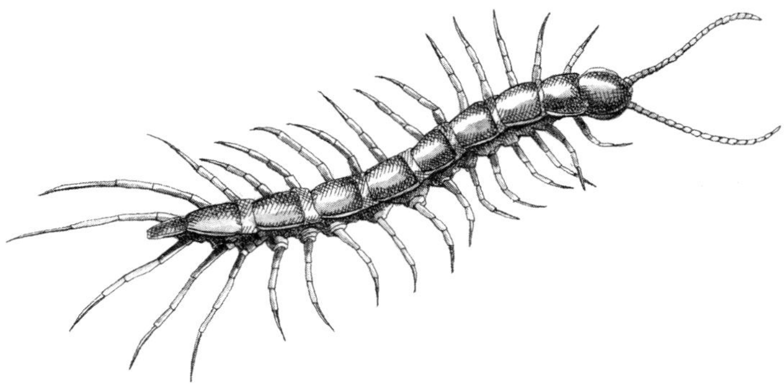

Using magnification, I have observed a host of tiny animals living in "wood-water" that I extracted by squeezing wet, pulpy wood with an old potato masher. I obtained turbid drops harboring a multitude of swirling and jittering microorganisms, among them spinning rotifers and slow-moving water bears, one-celled flagellates, ciliates, and amoebas.

Pioneer microbes create a thin substrate to which larger organisms take hold. The same species may not appear together again until another log falls with populations of organisms following the same general pattern of succession.

A visitor to the woods who inspects a fallen tree gets a glimpse of a special world. A rotting log can be viewed as a microcosm of the larger world – a classic integrated system of organisms and environment with familiar ecological forces on display in a chronological order. Almost every form of life appears: the decomposers, animal scavengers, and predators; primary producers such as photosynthetic algae; plant-eating herbivores, parasites, and commensals. They all live together in special relationships.

In time, certain parts of a log become almost indistinguishable from forest litter. Some parts bulge with mounds of moss that support clusters of ferns growing like green islands above the forest floor. Along the fallen giant's length, a birch sapling may start growing, its roots reaching around the softened trunk seeking anchorage in the soil below.

Like galaxies scattered throughout the cosmos, each log is an unknown entity. One never knows exactly what associations will develop, what specific conditions will be encountered, or what startling creatures and plants will appear when the log is turned or opened. Each decaying log becomes a world unto itself.

For a fun summer activity related to this essay, turn to page 204.

# july

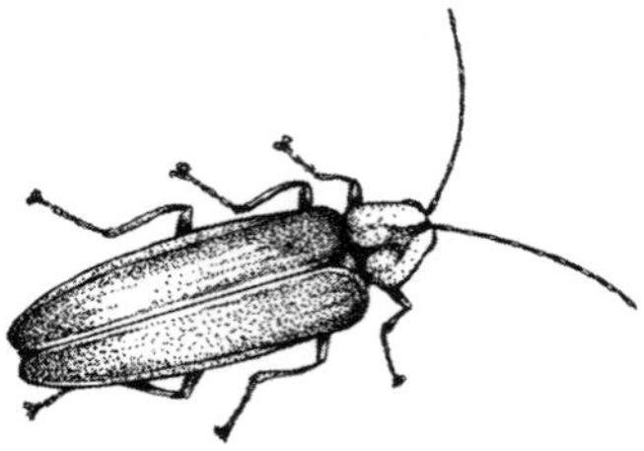



# first week

Each species of firefly has its own flash pattern. Males are sending luminescent signals to the flightless females hidden in the grass.

Cerceris wasps are flying. One of their prey items is the emerald ash borer and watching the wasps can reveal the invasive beetles' presence before they might otherwise be seen.

Young skunks are out and about.

The first barn swallow fledglings are catching their own food and the female is sitting on a new clutch.

# second week

Within 24 hours of hatching, and well before they can fly, wood ducklings drop many feet from the nest cavity to the water without injury.

Partridgeberry is blooming. The twin flowers of this little ground hugger will produce one fruit, but only if both flowers are pollinated.

Willow cone galls reach full size. Resembling pine cones, each gall began in late April when a small fly laid an egg in a willow terminal bud.

Broadwing hawk chicks will soon fledge. They often stand on the nest's edge.

# third week

Male bullfrogs have pale to bright yellow throats; in females it's pale to creamy white. A male's tympanum is larger than the eye; a female's is about the same size as the eye.

Roadsides are looking good if they are lined by Queen Anne's lace and chicory.

Cedar waxwings are feeding their young – mostly on fruits, but they'll take any caterpillars or leaf beetles that they see.

When submerged, the water boatman breathes from a bubble beneath its wings.



# fourth week

It's four bracts, not petals, that are now visible on bunchberry. Later, the bright red fruits of this tiny dogwood may be eaten by grouse, veeries, and vireos.

Tiny little toadlets are leaving ponds to take up a terrestrial existence. As tadpoles they were mostly vegetarians, but from now on they will be mostly carnivores.

Monarch butterflies return, just as milkweed begins to flower. They will lay their eggs on the undersides of milkweed leaves.

# Meat Eating Trees?

KENT P. MCFARLAND

Plants are not often thought of as predators. They're the nice guys. With over 300,000 species known to exist, only a small fraction are known to be meat-eaters. In our northern bogs, for example, insects are trapped on the sticky hairs of sundew or drowned in the pitcher plant's water.

Research now suggests that at least one *tree* may owe its size to more than just sun, water, and good soils.

The eastern white pine is one of the tallest native tree species in our region. Give them a few hundred years in ideal floodplain habitat, with roots sunk deep into sandy and silty soils and protected by hillsides from winds and lightning, and they'll grow to over 200 feet tall with nearly 8-foot-diameter trunks.

It takes a lot of energy and nutrients for a tree to grow to such grandeur. One thing that might help the eastern white pine is its surprising relationship with a meat-eating fungus.

The bicolored deceiver (*Laccaria bicolor*) appears above ground as a small, tan mushroom with lilac-colored gills. It is found in most coniferous woodlands throughout temperate regions around the globe. The fungus has a symbiotic relationship with many trees, including the eastern white pine. It forms a mycorrhizal sheath, like roots of the fungus, around the small root tips of the tree. The fungus receives sugars from the tree's photosynthesis that takes place above ground, while it supplies the plant with essential nutrients and helps to increase water uptake by the tree roots from below ground.

Such symbiotic relationships between trees and fungi are common. About 95 percent of plants get some nutrients from fungi, and fungi play a critical role in the food web. In particular, fungi (along with lightning strikes and soil bacteria) are critical for converting atmospheric nitrogen into reactive forms, such as nitrate and ammonia, which other living things can use for growth.

What makes the eastern white pine's relationship with the bicolored deceiver surprising is the way the tree benefits from the fungus' meat-eating habits. This discovery occurred by accident, during a study of tiny soil arthropods called springtails.

Many observers know springtails as snow fleas, the wingless insects often seen by the thousands jumping across the snow in late winter. They are incredibly small, but they can occur in huge numbers. Soil ecologists John Klironomos and Miranda Hart at the University of British Columbia wondered if springtails had an adverse effect on trees since they eat fungi that help to secure nutrients for many plants. They set up a simple experiment to feed the springtails a diet of fungi, including bicolored deceiver.

That's when their experiment took a strange turn. All of the springtails died when they were with bicolor deceiver. "It was as shocking as putting a pizza in front of a person and having the pizza eat the person instead of vice versa," Klironomos told *Science News.*

To confirm their findings, Klironomos and Hart fed a few hundred springtails a diet of bicolor deceiver while others were fed a diet either devoid of the fungus altogether or with another fungi species. After two weeks, only five percent of the springtails that were with bicolor deceiver remained alive. In contrast, nearly all the springtails that ate other species of fungi or whose diet was devoid of fungi survived.

The fungus was killing the springtails and breaking them down with a special enzyme. The researchers believe that the fungus first paralyzes the springtails with a toxin and then extends fine filaments into them to absorb nutrients.

So how does this make the eastern white pine tree a meat-eater? As a follow-up experiment, Klironomos and Hart fed a batch of springtails a diet with nitrogen that was tagged radioactively so they could follow it through the food web. The insects were added to containers of bicolor deceiver growing with white pine seedlings. After a few months they tested the seedlings and found that 25 percent of the nitrogen in the trees was radioactive, and thus had come directly from the springtails. It's as if white pine were fishermen using the fungus like a giant net to capture their prey.

Now, new research from scientists at Brock University in Ontario suggests that this adaptation may be shared by many plants. Green muscardine fungus, a soil-dwelling fungus found in many ecosystems, has long been known to infect insects. It has now been shown to associate with plant roots and transfer nitrogen from its insect prey to grass and even beans.

With webs of mycelia hunting tiny prey underground to help giants grow and capture the sun above, understanding who is eating whom just got a lot more complicated.

# A Moth "Settled in Quivering Contentment"

Bryan Pfeiffer

Like most of you, I spend my summer leisure time contemplating the tongue of the primrose moth.

Okay, it's not exactly a tongue. Butterflies and moths have a straw-like proboscis that they coil like a watch spring and unfurl to suck nectar from flowers. The primrose moth's proboscis is about half the length of its body. That anatomy alone might be enough to generate interest in this insect. But now consider that the primrose moth is Pepto Bismol pink with a lemony margin at the tips of its wings. In that pink presentation and probing proboscis, the primrose moth offers us a lesson in form, function, and evolution.

Primrose moths (*Schinia florida*) fly around searching for the evening primrose (*Oenothera biennis*), a common garden and roadside plant with a dangling, elegant yellow flower that opens at night and closes by day. A nighttime moth lingering in the flower until dawn gets an intimate embrace of petals.

Besides the hug, the moth gets nectar. I'm not actually sure what the plant gets out of this deal. The moth doesn't appear to pollinate evening primrose, according to botanists and scientific literature published on this particular encounter of insect and plant. In fact, the moth seems to get the best of this relationship. The female lays her eggs on the primrose, and when the caterpillars emerge they start munching the plant where it hurts – the flower buds.



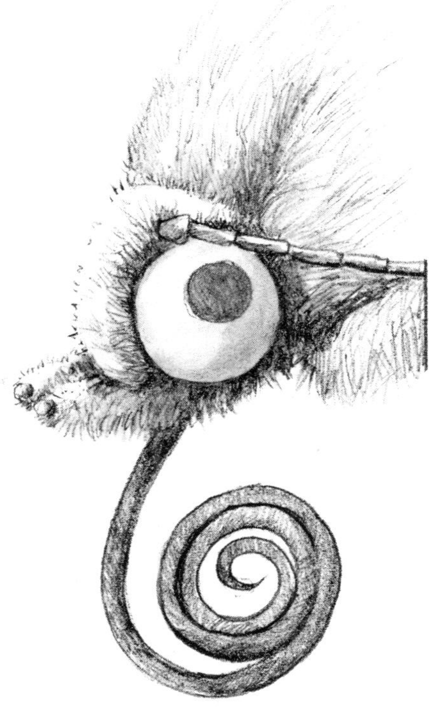

Although most of the action happens at night, alert flower-watchers can witness, in broad daylight, this intimate meeting of moth and bloom. It ranks among the countless examples of the struggle for existence and the powerful, shared evolution of insects and plants. If, like the moths themselves at night, you make the rounds to primrose flowers by day, every so often you will find your pink grail, still buried in a blossom after a night of binge-nectaring. The moth is like a drunk passed out at the bar at dawn, only tougher to locate than a drunk. The shocking pink is often hidden in the yellow petal embrace, with only the wings' yellow trailing edges still visible. Those edges resemble the yellow edges of the primrose petals. The moth has evolved with camouflage so that it can sit and drink nectar, and linger by day, presumably unnoticed by predators.

One of my favorite naturalists, William Hamilton Gibson, says we can hardly know the evening primrose until we know its nighttime visitor. Gibson was an exuberant nineteenth-century writer and illustrator. In his 1892 book *Sharp Eyes*, a collection of essays and illustrations through the seasons, which you must own, Gibson revels in the moth and its blossom:

> "Is this a mere withered, useless blossom that droops upon its stem? Is it not rather the prettiest luminous fairy tent that ever sheltered a day-dream? Last night, when its four green sepals burst from their cone, and sprang backward to release their bright, glossy petals, a small moth quickly caught the signal, and settled in quivering contentment, sipping at its throat. Its wings were of the purest rose-pink, bordered with yellow."

Gibson continues:

> "In the color of its marking, we find an outward expression of its beautiful sympathy, the yellow margins of the wings which protrude from the flower being quite primrose-like, and the pink being reflected in the rosy hue which the wilting primrose petals so often assume, especially at the throat."

Did you catch that "beautiful sympathy?" First, the yellow match: wing tips and petal. But a wilted primrose flower turns *pinkish*. So a primrose moth merely sitting on the stem of the plant may resemble an old flower and still find safety in the color pink. Evolution by means of natural selection (or so we assume).

What we cannot see in this little drama is the moth's proboscis lapping nectar from the base of a primrose blossom. But we can imagine or deduce it. Take a close look at the flower. It has a long, slender tube with nectar, called the hypanthium, below the base of the petals. It's a long reach for a moth seeking nectar. No matter. In nature form follows function. The moth unfurls its built-in drinking straw for a sweet reward, much as we depend on our drinking straw for that last half-inch of a favorite milkshake.

So, this July, get your favorite milkshake or maple creamee to go – and enjoy it in the good company of the primrose and its illustrious visitor.

# How the Trout Got Its Spots

TIM TRAVER

When I was 10, I frequently carried a tin can of worms and a battered fishing rod to the wild shores of Brickyard Pond, in the woods behind our subdivision. We caught mostly scrappy sunfish and white perch, with the occasional bass thrown in. There were alewives in some of the brooks, too, and we caught them with nets. As for the pretty trout that came from the hatchery truck, I never caught one. The fish I caught were mostly round, dark green or gray, and mottled like the mud and sand bottom of the pond.

Then, one day, a friend's older brother, a real fisherman with a green fishing vest, caught a large brown trout. I couldn't believe my eyes. The fish, shaped like a torpedo, was a yellowish gold and it had big red spots on its sides. Years later, I caught my first brook trout on a fly rod at Shoal Pond in the White Mountains. Again, I was mesmerized by the intense colors: the yellow and red spots, some with bluish halos; the fins that were bright red with white and black trim.

It all begs the question: why the trout's fancy colors when so many other fish are dishwater dull?

Part of the answer can be found in the biological record. Trout are part of the salmon family, which diverged from other bony fishes at the end of the Oligocene, about 30 million years ago. This was a time of global cooling, which suited the trout just fine. They were coldwater pioneers that pushed into higher-elevation watersheds to spawn and sometimes reside. Brook trout, our native trout, are part of the char genus (Salvelinus) and among the most cold-tolerant fish, able to live in glacial meltwater and isolated mountain lakes that stay frozen much of the year. As the last glacier melted and receded from the Northeast – about 10,000 years ago – brook trout migrated along the edge of the retreating ice, occupying enormous glacial bays, dammed glacial lakes, and northern rivers and streams.



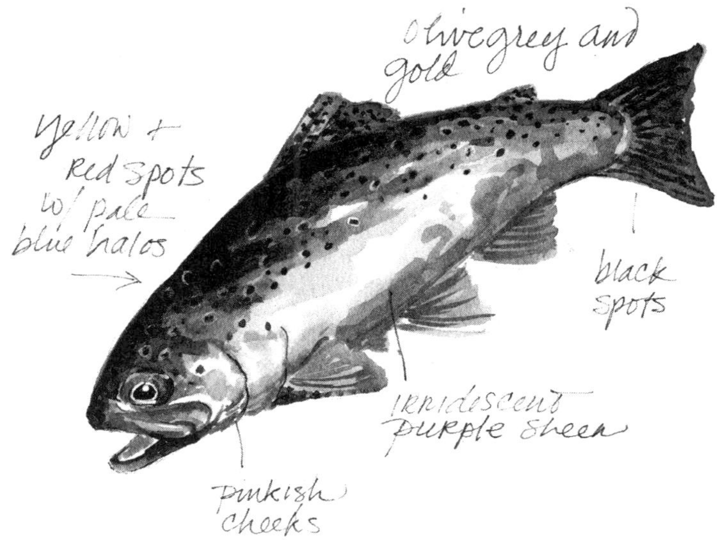

Where the water is clear and cold, bright colors can be seen. There is an advantage to this. Trout are territorial, and males and females aggressively defend feeding stations. They flash their colors in lateral and frontal threat displays, and if that doesn't work to push off intruders, they nip and chase each other to defend their position in a stream.

Color and pigment patterns seem to matter during fall spawning, too. The fins and bellies of brook trout, like the maple leaves above, turn orange in the fall. While shortened day length triggers spawning behavior, it's the trout's heightened color that brings on the aggression as males vie for the opportunity to be closest to an egg-laying female. The largest, most brightly colored males will most effectively fend off the peripheral males. These males are not just rivals, they also cannibalize the eggs.

Bright color can be a disadvantage, of course, especially to an animal that must be constantly wary of predation from above. So trout have evolved a two-toned skin. The bright threatening flash of their silvery sides – in rainbow trout, the silver is superimposed by a brushwork of red – contrasts with a dark back, engraved with ornate markings called vermiculations. These speckled patterns break up reflected light, merging trout with the gravelly substrate below. In moving water, trout are nearly invisible from above.

Environmental factors also influence a trout's colors. Food supply, for example, can have a major effect. Whether a brook trout has a pale or a pink belly is partly a function of how many crustaceans – small crayfish and shrimp – it eats. Brook trout that spend part of the year in the ocean take on a bluish hue, while trout living in the acidified waters of isolated beaver ponds are often deep yellow, closer to the tannin leachates that turn such waters brown. Chemical pollution may influence trout pigmentation, too. Chemicals found in certain antifouling boat-bottom paints turn rainbow trout paler. Hybridization adds to the puzzle of fish pigmentation. The High Sierra's golden trout, arguably the prettiest trout in the world, hybridize with west slope cutthroats to make a fish that fishermen call "cutgolds." The fact that we've been busy introducing trout to waters everywhere since the 1850s has muddled the color palette even more.

Looks can be deceiving, and maybe we put too much stock in beauty. But there's an ecological lesson in a trout's good looks. These fish are decked out in sky, sunshine, and the multi-hued gravels of the places they call home. They're a sentinel species: as goes the cold, clean water, so go the trout.

# The Grisly Business of Parasitoids

Virginia Barlow

At this time of year, it's the caterpillars eating leaves in the garden and the deer flies after our blood that get most of our attention. But behind the scenes are many insects that eat *other insects*, and among them is a group called the parasitoids, a clan that includes some rather demonic members.

A parasitoid develops on a single host and kills the host in the process. Parasites, on the other hand, tend to nibble on their hosts without killing them. And predators typically kill more than one of their prey items.

Because most parasitoids spend much of their lives buried within the bodies of their victims, they don't attract a lot of attention. But they are abundant and serve an important role in natural ecosystems, especially in agriculture, where they influence or regulate the population density of many of their hosts.

When a parasitoid kills its host, it can indeed be a grisly business. Typically, an adult female parasitoid lays an egg on the surface of, or into, the body of a living larva of another insect. When the egg hatches, the parasitoid proceeds to systematically consume the host. Like a cat with a mouse, it keeps its victim alive as long as possible. Dead larvae rot quickly, and this ruins the meal. So first the parasitoid eats the fat bodies of the larva, then the digestive organs, keeping the heart and central nervous system intact for as long as possible. Finally, these are consumed as well and the long-suffering victim dies, leaving an empty caterpillar shell in which the victorious insect may choose to pupate.

The slow death inflicted by parasitoids that attack other insects (and sometimes spiders) tested the concept of a benevolent God for nineteenth-century theologians who discussed this practice at length.

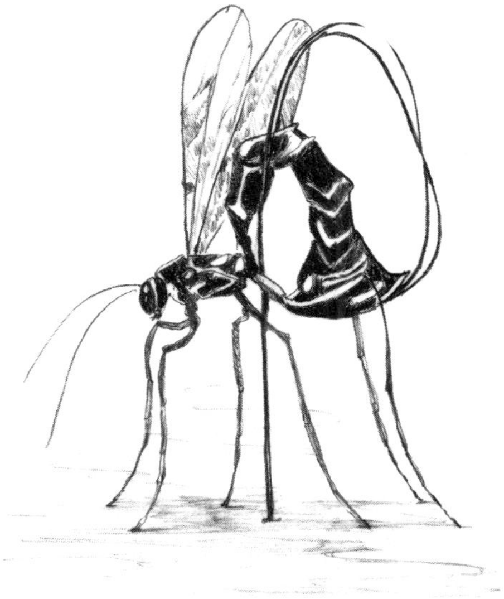

Even Darwin had trouble with the largest parasitoid family, as he wrote to Asa Gray in 1860: "I cannot persuade myself that a beneficent and omnipotent God would have designedly created the Ichneumonidae with the express intention of their feeding within the living bodies of Caterpillars…."

The female giant ichneumon wasp (*Megarhyssa macrurus*) is a striking animal, two inches long, boldly patterned in brown, orange, and yellow. Her two- to four-inch-long ovipositor with its two protective filaments looks like three long tails. Some parasitoids can choose to lay their eggs on a variety of host species, but giant ichneumon wasps need to find a larva of a pigeon horntail (*Tremex columba*), which is also a kind of wasp. Nothing else will do.

There is intense selective pressure on both of these insects to outwit the other. When a horntail female lays her egg in a tree, she includes both a fungus and a mucus secretion that promotes fungal growth, thus enabling her larva to burrow deeply into the wood. While this defensive strategy may once have given the horntail an advantage, the clever ichneumon soon figured out how to zero in on the very fungus that the horntail has enlisted. Once a female Megarhyssa arrives at the promising tree, she appears to use her antennae to sense the vibrations of her potential host.

She walks slowly over the bark, her antennae busily going back and forth, before drilling commences. Drilling might take half an hour, as the ovipositor is slowly pushed through up to four inches of solid wood.

The ichneumon ovipositor is incredibly slender, not much thicker than a horse hair, and the egg that passes through it is, by necessity, deformed into a slender, threadlike shape. But the process of finding a horntail, drilling a hole, and inserting an egg does not always result in a next ichneumon generation.

Other ichneumon wasps, of species that are unable to drill such holes themselves, may use Megarhyssa holes to insert their own eggs. When these hatch, the larvae destroy the Megarhyssa eggs and proceed to consume the horntail larva themselves.

An appealing host larva may have several parasitoid species competing for its nourishing tissues. In addition, many parasitoids have evolved to prey only on other parasitoids; these are called hyperparasitoids. And, amazingly, some hyperparasitoids are themselves attacked by parasitoids – making an extremely long food chain.

There is great variation in the behavior, shape, and size of insects that survive by consuming their brethren in this way. A tiny egg parasitoid in the wasp family Mymaridae, at one eight-thousandth of an inch long, may be the world's smallest insect.

It is thought that this lifestyle may have developed in the distant past from insects that consumed dead prey. Some entomologists believe that around 20 percent of all insect species now living are parasitoids. The insect order that includes wasps and bees has the greatest number, but there are many parasitoid flies as well, along with the occasional beetle or moth.

# Sundews, Pitcher Plants, and Bladderworts: Carnivorous Plants in our Midst

Anne Margolis

Some have teeth, some a sticky, entrapping liquid. Others have one-way tunnels leading to pools of digestive juices and are said to exude a paralyzing perfume. All of which are good reasons to beware in the vicinity of carnivorous plants – if you're an insect, that is, or maybe even a slug or worm. Anything larger is mostly safe from the specialized adaptations that sundews, pitcher plants, and bladderworts – the most common carnivorous plants in Vermont and New Hampshire – have evolved to obtain nutrients in the impoverished, acidic wetland habitats they inhabit.

Unfortunately for curious naturalists, the one with teeth (really modified leaf margins) – the Venus flytrap – is not found in the wild around here. The less well known but truly beautiful sundew, which is found in this area, also uses its leaves – evolved into red, glistening paddles in a feat of evolutionary ingenuity – to nab passing insects. Sundews are named for their "sparkle," which comes from tiny droplets of moisture exuded by this diminutive plant's leaves. This moisture is not benign dew, as the name suggests, but sticky mucus that attracts the attention of passing insects who then approach, usually too close, to investigate. Once the insect makes contact with the mucus, it is trapped, and the sundew's tentacle-like, modified leaf curls inward to smother and begin digesting it. The resulting insect slurry is then absorbed by special glands on the leaf's surface.

Pitcher plants, too, slowly digest their insect prey, albeit within a pool of juice that breaks the insect down into its nutritional components. Instead of advertising with sparkling dewdrops, pitcher plants instead emit an attractive perfume. Like the cartoon dog drawn to a freshly baked pie on a ribbon of scent, an insect is lured ever closer to a pitcher plant's pitchers, also modified from leaves. Lured by the promise of sweet nectar, an insect ventures heedlessly into the pitcher's depths. Alas, once inside the entrance, the hapless fellow has taken his last steps; he may realize his folly and attempt to climb or fly out, but the downward-pointing hairs, waxy coating, and snug entrance to the pitcher will defeat his efforts until, exhausted, he falls into the pool and is slowly absorbed. Frogs will often perch at pitcher entrances, hoping for an easy meal; the predator becomes the prey on occasion, as evidenced by frog skeletons found in pitchers by prying botanists.

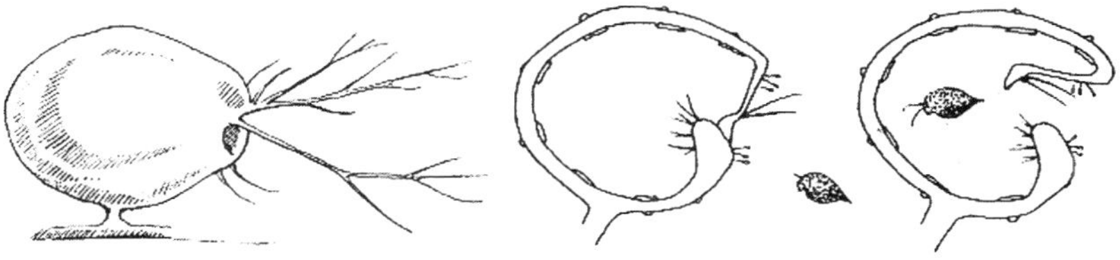

Bladderwort

The last of our common carnivorous plants, the bladderwort, is by comparison an accidental consumer. No dew, no fragrance, just chance – although some scientists speculate that the sugary mucus this plant excretes may in fact attract prey. Bladderworts form tangled, floating mats on the surfaces of water bodies, full of thousands of nearly invisible, bladder-like appendages. Each bladder maintains a negative pressure inside, such that its walls are slightly indented. At the flap that seals the bladder shut, pointy hairs thrust into the water, and when microscopic insects and animals brush the hairs, the bladder door is triggered to spring open. Water rushes into the bladder as the inside and outside pressures equalize. The door snaps shut again, and any tiny prey that have been sucked in swim around until they run out of air, food, or both, at which time natural decomposition breaks them down for the benefit of the bladderwort.

While these three hardy, insect-eating plants may seem to have cunning, premeditated feeding methods, their actions are truly just an evolutionary product of their environment: acidic waters, such as those found in bogs. Bogs are a specific sort of wetland with very low nutrient levels. Pitcher plants, sundews, and bladderworts lend life to an otherwise low-diversity wetland, but to live, they must reap an unconventional source of nutrients. To do so, they have sacrificed deep roots and highly photosynthetic leaves – truly a risky tradeoff since, like all green plants, carnivorous plants attain vital carbohydrates from photosynthesis. The insects serve as a reservoir of nutrients normally found in soil but lacking in acid waters, such as nitrogen and phosphorus.

Unfortunately, many of our bogs and other wetlands are being lost to construction activities and other causes of wetland draining. Increasingly, carnivorous plants are forced to live in ever smaller "islands" of suitable habitat. Someday, they may not be as easy to find, or to marvel over as a reminder that not all plants follow convention.

To find members of this odd trio, look no farther than your nearest bog or other acidic wetland. Land trusts and conservancies are especially interested in wetland conservation, so it may help to check with one in your local area.

# Beetles and Bubbles, Above and Below

KENRICK VEZINA

Every morning, my pool is the scene of six-legged tragedies: chunky beetles puttering around on the surface, looking for a leaf-cum-life preserver; a few flies long since deceased. Once, the surface was peppered with black commas. These turned out to be winged ants, unlucky breeders from a nearby colony that must have swarmed. Each morning the suite of insects is different, but the result is almost always mass death.

To creatures so large as ourselves, a pool's surface tension offers only token resistance. Insects, however, find themselves in a very awkward place. Lest one forget the importance of scale in the animal kingdom, take this bit from biologist J.B.S. Haldane's essay *On Being the Right Size*: "You can drop a mouse down a thousand-yard mine shaft; and, on arriving at the bottom, it gets a slight shock and walks away. A rat is killed, a man is broken, a horse splashes." An insect, of course, can fall the same distance with impunity for the same reasons many of them can cling to walls and ceilings. Gravity is a trivial matter; falling is a non-risk. Water, on the other hand, is a huge risk. Haldane, in paraphrase: A man coming out of a pool has to carry a thin film of water that weighs roughly a pound; a mouse carries roughly its own weight, and a fly has to carry many times its own body weight.

Yet not all insects are doomed by water. Many species live on, in, or under the surface, and dealing strictly in beetles, there are several families of water-lovers. You've likely seen one or two beetles in the water near the edge of a local pond. Aquatic beetles vary, but they're generally of modest proportions with brownish or blackish coloration and oval-shaped bodies. Their blandness belies the ingenious tricks that they and other water-dwelling insects have developed to turn surface tension and their physics of being small to their advantage.

Bubbles are one such trick; some beetles use their outer wings to trap these little sources of oxygen against their backs, others carry bubbles at the tips of their posteriors.

Bullet-shaped predaceous diving beetles (family Dytiscidae) must return to the surface now and then, to refresh their bubbles before kicking beneath the surface using the long hairs on their backmost legs, in search of prey ranging from tadpoles to small fish. These bubbles, you might think, are a terribly short-term solution to the need for oxygen underwater, but they last longer than you'd expect.

This comes back, as Haldane wrote, to being the right size. Insects are small enough that they can forego lungs. Instead, they have tiny holes in their exoskeletons called spiracles. These lead to tiny tubes, which branch into even tinier tubes. Insects do not "breathe" through these tubes in an active sense; they simply let oxygen diffuse directly into their tissues from the air around them.

Diffusion is also key to the remarkable endurance of many bubble-bearing beetles. As a beetle uses up the oxygen in its pocket of air, some of the dissolved oxygen in the surrounding water diffuses into the comparatively oxygen-poor bubble. Some beetles, like the riffle beetles (family Elmidae) – small black beetles that are found in fast-moving, highly oxygenated waters – are true masters of the bubble. They have nets of special, water-repellent hairs that keep a thin film of air trapped against their bodies. Their bubble is kept at a fixed volume; water is never allowed to encroach. The result is a constant influx of oxygen from the water to maintain this volume. They have exploited the physics at work on their small scale to create a functional gill.

Of course, these true water beetles never find their way into my pool – it lacks food or cover, among other things. Now, though, when I gaze across the surface, it's hard not to see the wonder and drama implied by this watery trap. It may just be a cheap above-ground swimming pool, but it's emblematic of a life where water meets sky, where the physics of size meets surface tension, and where life meets death.

# august

## first week

Flickers on the ground are probably eating ants, their favorite insect prey. A researcher once counted 5,000 ants in the stomach of a single flicker.

Most of a dragonfly's one- to four-year lifespan is spent underwater as a predatory larva. The airborne phase lasts for only a few weeks.

A birdwatching hiatus, as most songbirds have stopped singing, but haven't yet begun to migrate.

Check the woods for woodland asters, the first of the asters to bloom.

## second week

Perseid meteor shower peaks.
This is one of the best meteor showers, especially if there are no clouds and no moon.

Chipmunks are taking a break, staying underground and eating stored seeds.

Luckily for us, hermit thrushes have an extended breeding season and will continue to sing their lovely song after most other birds have fallen silent.

Though wood turtles are usually seen in uplands, they spend more time in thick vegetation near water.

# third week

Many birds molt after breeding and before migrating. They may look very ratty.

Some tobacco hornworms grow to be four inches long but those that are being fed on by the larvae of parasitoid wasps are small. The numerous little white pupal cases of the wasps are often seen on the caterpillars' backs at this time of year.

After they are pollinated, Indian pipes straighten up and don't look like white pipes anymore. Before long they'll turn black.

# fourth week

Birds are quieter and crickets are noisier.

Jewelweed seeds are being propelled up to four feet from their capsules. They are annuals, unlike the vast majority of wildflowers.

Red efts, the terrestrial phase of the eastern red-spotted newt, have grown tougher skin, lost their gills, and traded in their paddle tails for a more rod-like version.

Reddish hues begin to appear on Virginia creeper, sumac, and red maple.

Long summer evenings are no longer long.

# Butterflies at the Bar

Susan Shea

Toddlers aren't the only ones fond of mud puddles. Butterflies and moths often gather at puddles in large groups. I witnessed about 30 tiger swallowtail butterflies around a puddle on a woods road one spring, their yellow, black-veined wings twitching slightly, contrasting with the brown mud. Another time I saw a crowd of swallowtails around a pile of damp wood ashes in my yard.

This curious behavior is known as "puddling." Although butterflies and moths get most of their nutrition from flower nectar, puddling provides another way to obtain nutrients, and replenish fluids. The insects use their long tongues, called proboscises, to deliver the fluid or other material into their mouths.

Some species puddle on scat and carrion. This can be shocking to human sensibilities. I was a bit taken aback the first time I saw a beautiful tiger swallowtail on a fresh pile of manure. Kent McFarland, a conservation biologist at the Vermont Center for Ecostudies, recalled seeing a harvester butterfly on a pile of coyote scat.

Fermenting fruit is another butterfly favorite. We have an old apple tree that shades our driveway. In the fall I have to pull my car in slowly so as not to hit all the white admirals – black-winged butterflies with white bands and red and blue dots. They seem to love the crushed, rotting apples.

What nutrients do butterflies obtain through puddling? Salt is probably the most important one. Sodium tends to be scarce in the adult butterfly diet and is essential for reproduction and flight. McFarland has seen groups of up to a thousand white admirals on the back roads of Vermont's Northeast Kingdom in spring, feeding on road salt left from the winter. "So many butterflies that you can't drive on the road without killing them," he said. Butterflies may also obtain proteins and minerals from this behavior.

Many species in our region puddle. In addition to the swallowtails and admirals, these include members of the whites and sulphurs family, as well as a number of the brushfoots, including mourning cloaks, question marks, and eastern commas.

Although both male and female butterflies are known to puddle, the activity is primarily a male behavior. One reason appears to relate to reproduction. In experiments, scientists attracted male butterflies to sand soaked with sodium. At least in some species studied, males have been found to transfer sodium to females during mating. The males delivered the sodium via the spermatophore, a package that contains the sperm, making a "nuptial gift." Females incorporated the element into their eggs and, at least in one species studied, the presence of sodium increased egg production. Receiving sodium from males frees females from the risks of predation that puddling on the ground can entail.

Another reason for the predominance of male butterfly puddling may be the differences in energy requirements between the genders. Sodium is critical for neuromuscular activity in butterflies. Males may have a greater need for sodium because they spend more time in flight than females and tend to be quicker.

Why do butterflies cluster in groups while puddling? It may be a simple case of social facilitation – one butterfly finds the resource, others see it and follow. Clustering also reduces the risk of predation to any one individual. These congregations may also make males more conspicuous to females looking for mates.

Puddling behavior is not unique to the Northeast. It is common around the world, although feeding preferences vary among butterfly species, as do nutritional needs. "In the tropics, you can get amazing hordes along rivers," said McFarland. Certain exotic moths engage in weird puddling behaviors. A moth found in Madagascar sucks tears by inserting its proboscis into the closed eyelids of roosting birds. Cases of moths drinking human tears have been reported from Thailand. Some species of Russian moths are known as "vampire moths" – they drill their barbed tongues under the skin of sleeping animals (including humans) to suck blood. Fortunately, our New England butterflies and moths refrain from such activities.

It's easy to make a puddling area in your flower garden. Place a shallow basin of water containing a pinch or two of salt on the ground. Also try putting out a tray of fruit that is past its prime (though be forewarned that this may also attract bees). Watch for butterflies and see if you can spot their long tongues through your binoculars.

For a fun summer activity related to this essay, turn to page 206.

# The Touchy-Feely World of Whiskers

Li Shen

Of the many questions one is left with after listening to the nursery rhyme *Three Blind Mice*, none is more vexing than how three blind rodents were able to chase anything, let alone a farmer's wife. As the three mice in question died in 1805, we'll probably never know the full answer. There are some clues in the scientific record, though. The fact is, mice and other nocturnal rodents can take in sophisticated three-dimensional information about their surroundings without using their eyes.

Rodent eyes don't function like our eyes. Ours are on the front of our head and we see in stereo; their eyes are on the side of their head and their field of vision doesn't overlap. Our eyes always move together; a rodent's eyes can move in opposite directions. If a rat points its snout downward, its eyes look up, rather than where its nose is pointing. If its head tilts down to the right, the right eye looks up while the left eye looks down.

There is a purpose to these odd movements: to keep the space above in view at all times. To a rodent, constant scanning overhead for birds of prey is more important for survival than clearly seeing the path ahead.

So how do rats sense what's in front of their noses? Instead of relying on sight, they pass their whiskers over all surfaces repeatedly from different angles to get three-dimensional images of their surroundings. This process, called "whisking," occurs constantly and rapidly – up to 12 times per second, among the fastest movements measured in mammals. Each whisker has its own muscle and can move independently. There are also muscle arrays that move all the whiskers together.

If you were to examine a rat's face, you would see that it has two different varieties of facial hair: long, stiff whiskers that stick out around the snout and above the eyes, and shorter, finer whiskers below the nostrils that point down. The whiskers are arranged in a defined grid pattern. If you could peer into the rat's head, you would discover that each whisker is connected to a discrete bundle of brain cells. These bundles are arranged in exactly the same grid pattern as the whiskers to which they are connected. This organization of sensors provides the rat with a detailed "snapshot" of the space in front of it.

Whiskers themselves are not living tissue. Their exquisite sensitivity lies at the base, in the follicle where the whisker sprouts from the skin. When a whisker touches a surface, it bends. The tension from bending is sensed by nerves in the follicle that send a signal to the brain.

While the bending of whiskers transmits spatial information, the sensitivity of whiskers to vibration allows the rat to feel differences in texture with astonishing accuracy. Whiskers are far more sensitive than the human fingertip – for instance, a rat can tell the difference between a totally smooth surface and one scored with microscopic grooves 30 microns deep (a micron being one thousandth of a millimeter).

Different whiskers resonate with different frequencies of sound. The thicker, longer whiskers away from the nose vibrate at lower frequencies, while the shorter, finer whiskers closer to the nose respond to higher frequencies. Like strings on a piano, the whiskers form an orderly array of filaments tuned to a gradation of sounds, or vibrations, from low to high. It is also likely that whiskers sense air currents in burrows and narrow spaces for additional directional clues.

Whiskers, of course, do not operate in isolation. The rat senses its environment through hearing and smell, too. In fact, whisking and smelling, or sniffing, are locked into the same rhythm, so that every time a rat whisks it also sniffs. Thus, a shape, texture, and smell "snapshot" is transmitted simultaneously to the brain.

All of which is to say that three blind mice, rats, or other whisking creatures wouldn't be nearly as helpless as one might expect. While out in the open they might be easy prey for a hawk, or the farmer's wife, in other contexts they could navigate well without sight. For a life often lived in shadows, scurrying beneath vegetation and navigating burrows, the touchy-feely sense of whisking offers a rich way to "see" that isn't dependent on eyes.

# Blackberry Season

Rachel Sargent

The bank in front of our house is a dense tangle of arching canes and thorns as large as cat claws. I wriggle further in, lips pressed against the pain of scratches and fingers straining for that last, fattest, blackest berry. I brush it, and it falls into the gloom of leaves and grass, never to be retrieved. Disentangling myself, I take my bowl of berry plunder back to the house where my dad will make the best pie I know: wild blackberry.

Wild blackberries are delicious, grow like weeds, and ripen in August, just in time for my birthday. They belong to the rose family along with raspberries, strawberries, the stone fruits, and, unexpectedly, almonds.

It is unlikely to surprise anyone that blackberries are closely related to raspberries. People often mistake black raspberries for blackberries, but there are easy, tell-tale differences between these plants. Here's the quick and dirty way of distinguishing between them: both black and red raspberries pull off their stems completely, leaving hollow or dome-shaped fruits, while blackberries have fleshy cores, making them more solid.

When the plants aren't fruiting, they are much more difficult to tell apart. Both grow as a tangle of canes with compound leaves of three to five leaflets. However, again, a closer look reveals differences. The thorns of blackberries are straight while black raspberry thorns are hooked. Both berries have white flowers with five petals, but the petals of blackberry flowers spread out to look like a five-pointed star, while black raspberry flowers have stubbier, close-set petals giving the whole flower a rounder shape.

AUG

In one of those ironic twists of botany, despite their name, blackberries are not considered berries at all. They are aggregate fruits made up of juicy little spheres called drupelets. Aggregate fruits come from a single flower, but each carpel (the female part of a flower) forms a fleshy fruit with a stony covering over the seed. The seeds in the drupelets of blackberries are so small that they are hard to see, but you can imagine all those little seed pips as itty-bitty peach pits. A true berry, as a botanist would define one, is a fleshy fruit produced from one ovary in the flower. This means strawberries aren't berries either, but blueberries really are berries. And to further confuse you, so are tomatoes and bananas. (Botanists like to make fruit difficult for the rest of us).

The rich, dark color that gives blackberries their name comes from a group of organic compounds called anthocyanins. Anthocyanins are common plant pigments, ranging from red to purple to blue, depending on the pH the pigment is exposed to in the plant's tissues. Red autumn leaves, purple pansies, and blueberries all owe their color to anthocyanins. In flowers, the anthocyanin color is used to say "Here I am! Pollinate me!" In fruits, its message is, "eat my seeds!" Not only do blackberries use anthocyanins to advertise when they are ripe, they have something called "pre-ripening fruit flags." That means they go through several color changes, from green to white to red, before finally ripening to black. These pre-ripening colors are signals (or flags) to animals that the berries will be ready soon.

Anthocyanins do more than just make pretty colors. They can act as a kind of plant sunscreen, blocking blue-green and ultraviolet wavelengths that can damage sensitive tissues. This is why new leaves have red anthocyanins in them, even though, unlike fruits, they do not want to be eaten. And as a final perk, anthocyanins are powerful antioxidants, so don't feel so guilty about sneaking that extra piece of blackberry pie.

People aren't the only ones who love to eat blackberries. Many times out picking, I've had a show-down with a beetle, ant, or slug over just which of us will get a berry. Of course, larger animals – birds, bears, rodents, and other wildlife – eat blackberries too, and play an important role in dispersing seeds through defecation. By hitch-hiking inside an animal, blackberry seeds can travel long distances. This is the reason plants often seem to spring up overnight, as soon as there's an open spot in the woods for them. I've seen this effect close to home, although not with wildlife. My dog loves blackberries and will eat them right off the canes. Thanks to her, we now have blackberries in far-flung patches around the house.

# Why are Moose so Nosy?

LISA OLNEY

The silhouette of a moose is noticeably different from that of its deer cousins. Its bulky, hunched body sits on tall, improbably proportioned legs. And then there's that nose. It's long and broad – a full 65 percent of the moose's head length – with enlarged nostrils that are positioned not in the front of the face, but off to the sides. By the nose alone, there's little chance of mistaking Bullwinkle for Bambi.

There are traditional explanations for the moose's unusual nose. Wabanaki tribes share tales of the hero Gluskap, who squeezed the moose, shrinking him from a giant's size and creating an animal with a bulging proboscis. As for a scientific explanation, recent research suggests at least two possibilities.

Dr. Lawrence Witmer of Ohio University conducted an extensive study of the animals' narial (nose) anatomy. Working with roadkill moose heads, and also the heads of whitetail deer, he used both simple dissection techniques and high-tech approaches such as CT scanning to compare the two animals. His research, first published in 2004, suggests that moose noses may have at least two advantages that other deer, and most other mammals, lack: stereolfaction and waterproof nasal passages.

To understand stereolfaction, consider the way that humans see. Each one of our eyes takes in a distinct field of vision, which, when combined in the brain, allows us to determine distance. Stereolfaction involves a similar process, except that it's based on the sense of smell. According to Witmer, "moose, with their widely separated nostrils, may have enough separation that each nostril samples a different part of a gradient, allowing the animal to orient easily and track odors." In other words, thanks to their big noses, moose may be receiving two fields of scent, strengthening their ability to determine the location and distance of smells.

This heightened sense of smell would be helpful in searching for food or danger, and also, perhaps, in mating. Moose rely on long-distance scent detection to coordinate mating, so there is a strong evolutionary reason for them to have developed a special ability to track down a scent's direction.

A second finding of Witmer's study is that there are specialized structures within moose nostrils that automatically seal off the nose from water. According to Witmer, "mammals all tend to be able to open their nostrils (like humans "flaring" their nostrils), but relatively few can close them with muscles. Moose seem to do it not with muscles but rather by expanding the size of a pad of connective tissue due to the pressure of water."

This adaptation has obvious advantages for moose, which are far more dependent on aquatic habitats than other deer species. They consume large amounts of aquatic vegetation, and it's not uncommon to see moose standing in the middle of wetlands, their heads fully submerged as they graze on underwater plants. Aquatic habitats also provide moose refuge from insects and from heat: because of their size and thick coats, moose are especially susceptible to heat stress which, on a calm day, begins at just 62 degrees.

Moose are great swimmers, and can submerge completely for 30 seconds or more. They even dive, to depths of up to five meters – and their self-sealing nose facilitates this. "The deeper they dive, the greater the pressure, the tighter the seal," said Witmer. "It's basically a valve."

Of course, that's a scientist's take. The Penobscots of Maine and the Mic'Maqs of Nova Scotia both have creation myths that hold that moose came from the sea, originating from whales, and can return there for refuge.

Figuratively speaking, this might not be very far off.

# Apples in the Woods: Telling Wild from Tame

JOE RANKIN

Many times I've been wandering through dense forest only to stumble on human artifacts like old cellar holes, a well, or rusting farm equipment. Then there are the miles of stone walls running through mature woods.

These artifacts are a humbling reminder that we're not the first to come this way. Most of what remains from the abandoned homesteads is of the durable iron and stone variety, not the organic. But sometimes in the New England woods you stumble across evidence of human presence that's very much alive: apple trees.

Apples are natives of central Asia whose usefulness led humans to plant them around the globe. European colonists brought them to the New World in the early 1600s. At one time, almost every New England farm had a few apple trees.

The woods are dotted with relict apple trees – old, gnarled trunks hollowed by rot, leaning over as though tired. You could, naturally, assume that these trees were planted and once lovingly cared for, and most of the time you'd be correct. But, given that apples are pretty well naturalized in the U.S., how can you be sure?

Well, there are a few ways, and with a little observation and application of common sense, you should be able to tell with relative certainty, said John Bunker, the apple guy at Fedco Trees in Waterville, Maine. Bunker has spent more than 30 years learning about, promoting, identifying, and propagating apples.

One (almost) sure-fire way to tell a wild apple tree from a domestic one: "Look for the graft," said Bunker. Often on trees that are 100, 150, or even 200 years old, the graft union is still very visible near the base of the trunk, he said.

An apple seed will not produce a faithful reproduction of its parent tree (in the same way that you're not your father's identical twin), so orchardists use grafting to propagate desirable varieties. It's an old technique: the Chinese were doing it 4,000 years ago. Grafting involves replacing the growing shoot of a two-year-old "rootstock" tree with a piece of branch (the scion) from the desired variety. Cuts are made in scion and rootstock and the two pieces carefully spliced together with the cambium layers touching. The graft is usually wrapped with stretchy grafting tape.

At the graft union, there's usually a noticeable bulge or a depression in the trunk. "That is because the scion and the rootstock didn't have the same vigor," explains Bunker. Often the bark color is different on either side of the graft line, denoting the two varieties joined there.

Bunker cautions that sometimes you can find a grafted tree where the scion and rootstock were so close in vigor and bark color that the graft line isn't apparent. In such cases, another clue is the pattern of the branches. Are they regularly spaced? Are there old pruning scars or pruning cuts? Does the tree look like it's been shaped? "If you look at where the holes are, where the branches used to be, you can put together a picture of what that tree once looked like," Bunker said.

Are there other trees, or even stumps of apple trees, in the area? Two, three, or four trees of nearly the same age planted in a grid makes it more likely that these are the products of nurture, not nature. Similarly, Bunker says to consider the location. "Even knowing nothing about grafts or pruning, most woodlot owners could ask themselves, 'is it possible someone ever could have planted an apple tree in this spot?' and answer correctly, yes or no."

Another clue: How does the apple taste?

Of course, there are times when nature – and man – throws you a curve. Say there's no sign of the graft, but the tree looks like it's been shaped and it's in a spot where there could have been an orchard. Well, it might be a wild apple tree. Or it might be a seedling apple that someone planted. New Englanders did that a lot, particularly back in the early 1800s when most apples were used for making hard cider. Or it could be part of "nature's orchard" – an orchard where all of the original planted trees are gone and only their feral seedlings remain.

# Ambush in the Meadow

Steven Shepard

As a nature writer and photographer, I spend a lot of my time peering closely at leaves, twigs, and flowers, seeking what lurks in their midst. So it was that I discovered Phymata, the ambush bug. I was walking slowly through a meadow, bent over almost double as I carried a tripod-mounted camera instead of a magnifying glass. Spotting a fly on a daisy, I approached slowly, finding it odd that the insect didn't move away from me. Puzzled, I looked closer and found a small, bulbous-eyed bug, his mouthparts embedded in the fly.

Ambush bugs lurk in the foliage, waiting for prey to come near. When they spot a victim they leap from cover, impale the hapless creature with a penetrating beak, pump liquefying enzyme into its body, and slurp up dinner. Although their specialty is disguise, their appearance, revealed, is daunting. If they were blown up to the size of a car, they would put a Bradley Fighting Vehicle to shame. Armored and massively muscular, they easily capture and overpower prey many times their own size. Of course, a little perspective is in order: this is a bug that could easily fit on the real estate of my smallest fingernail, with plenty of room to maneuver.

Dr. David Punzalan, a postdoctoral fellow at the Royal Ontario Museum's Department of Natural History, has extensively researched ambush bugs. He explained that they are "generalist predators" that take a wide variety of prey that typically visit flowers. Wasps, flies, and butterflies are all on the hit list. Ambush bugs will prey on insects that are considerably larger than themselves, including bumblebees.

I asked about their preferred hunting grounds. "The bugs don't seem exceptionally picky about where they will hunt," Punzalan noted, "as long as the insect traffic in the area is high." Their location varies over time, in keeping with which wildflowers are blooming. In late summer and fall, favorite host plants include Queen Anne's lace, goldenrod, thistle, asters, daisies, and black-eyed susans.

Following my exchange with Dr. Punzalan, I returned to the meadow and searched a bit more diligently for Phymata. Sure enough, I found them on a variety of flowers, many of them in the act of enjoying dinner. They're beautiful: because of their angular shape they look almost prismatic, with colors ranging from emerald green to bicolored tan and gold.

In a subsequent email, Punzalan explained that some of the variation in color stems from sexual dimorphism (variations according to the sex of the organism), others from age. "Males are generally darker," he noted, "with some dark patches reduced or absent in females." This darker coloration appears to enable the males to better absorb heat energy from the sun, and thereby increase their mobility. Why this color differentiation exists between genders, however, is unclear.

In my second trip through the meadow, I had also noticed that on quite a few flowers, one ambush bug was perched atop another. "Piggybacking" is common, and symptomatic of the intense competition for females. This is not a mating behavior, but instead "mate-guarding" to prevent competing males from honing in on a chosen female. Males also engage in courtship behaviors that include twitching antennae, tapping forelegs, trembling pulses throughout their bodies, and rapid squeaking.

Squeaking? "Yes," Punzalan confirmed. "Both sexes can stridulate by scraping their beaks on a file under their thorax. In fact, immatures appear to employ this technique when they're alarmed. If you pick one up by the thorax and watch closely, you'll see rapid head-nodding, which is the scraping movement, and if you hold them close to your ear you can even hear it."

There are two species of ambush bug in the Northeast, *Phymata Americana* and *Phymata Pennsylvanica*, although the nomenclature is a bit contentious. Some authors have placed the two as related subspecies, while others consider them to be altogether separate species in spite of the fact that there has been no formal demonstration of genetic or behavioral isolation.

Whatever the case, these are fascinating little creatures. Next time you're out meadow-walking, take the time to look a little closer at the flowers that surround you. But beware: there are killers lurking.

# september

# first week

Blueberries are eaten by white-footed mice, chipmunks, skunks, and bears, as well as by many birds.

The snapping turtle eggs that were laid about three months ago are hatching. Some hatchlings head for the nearest pond, but others will remain in place until spring.

Honeybees are gathering nectar from goldenrods.

Mourning cloak butterflies are fattening up for hibernation. They overwinter as adults and can be seen flying in spring before the snow melts.

# second week

Dry days will cause milkweed pods to open, releasing streams of fluffy parachutes that are each attached to a seed. All the seeds in a pod are from just one flower; it's the rare flower that makes seeds.

Crickets may move into buildings as they search for places to hibernate. Their incessant chirping can be aggravating at close range.

It is quieter in fields and woods, now that fall migration is underway.

Beginning of the month-long moose mating season.

# third week

Loons are molting and most of them will have finished growing out their grayish-brown winter feathers before they migrate.

Fall dandelions (*Scorzoneroides autumnalis*) are blooming along roadsides. The flowers are similar to, but somewhat smaller than, the dandelions that bloom in the spring.

Beaked hazelnuts are ripe, but squirrels and chipmunks are likely to get to them before you do. Moose, deer, hare, rabbit, and beaver eat other parts of this shrub.

# fourth week

Whitetail bucks tear away the velvet on their antlers and polish them by thrashing them against shrubs and low branches.

Common green darners are known to migrate more than 400 miles over a period of two months. This usually takes place between August and November.

Catbirds are fattening up on almost any fruit or berry you can think of. They will soon leave to winter from the Gulf Coast south to Costa Rica.

Crows are collecting and stashing acorns.

# How Could a Fish Survive *That*?

Dave Mance III

There were times in August 2011, during Tropical Storm Irene, when the rivers in Vermont and New Hampshire seemed to be made out of something other than water. Whatever it was was viscous and liquid, sure, but that roiling, furious, chocolate-colored mass was unlike anything many of us had ever seen before. When we talk of river water we usually use words like *sing*; river stewards have been known to take things to worshipful extremes and use words like *amniotic*. But this.... This fecal, angry substance carrying cars and horizontal trees was something else entirely.

Watching the raw power of the river water in the aftermath of Irene, it was impossible not to think of the animals that live there. How on earth could a trout survive? If each foot of rising water produces 500 pounds of lateral force, then wouldn't every single living thing be swept away in such a torrent?

Talk to a fisheries biologist and you'll learn that the answer is "no, but." The "no" part can be chalked up to physics, among other factors. A trout's streamlined shape minimizes resistance, and its slimy epidermis cuts down on water friction. They hug the bottom of the stream during a flood, where things are slower and less turbulent than higher in the water column. They hide behind rocks and snags and in pockets inside stream banks where the natural structure decreases the velocity of the water, much as humans might use a building as a windbreak. And when all else fails, they get out of Dodge and seek slower water outside the stream channel, a move that can lead to stranding if the water level drops too quickly.

The "but" part of the answer reflects the fact that some fish don't make it. Biologist Rich Kirn, with the Vermont Fish and Wildlife Department, says that with a normal-sized flood he'd expect to see some decline in fish stocks, but Irene was above and beyond normal. Vermont has monitored fish populations at stations throughout the state for the past few decades. Kirn says that biologists had already noticed some decline in salmonid populations due to the spring flooding in northern and central areas of the state in 2011, and forecast more in the wake of Irene. Fortunately, Irene's flash flooding was late enough in the year that the hatchlings stood a fighting chance. Late spring floods in May and June can be especially hard on trout populations, as the just-hatched fry are especially vulnerable.

The length of time it takes the animal life in a river to recover depends on how much damage occurs during a storm. In areas where the riparian vegetation is wiped out and the river channel inundated with sediment, or, conversely, scoured raw, it might take years, if not decades. New Hampshire fisheries biologist Jason Carrier points to the Nash Stream in northern New Hampshire – where years of poor river management, coupled with a dam break and subsequent flood in 1969 left the river in a moonscape condition – as an example of a catastrophic flood we're still recovering from. New Hampshire Fish and Game, Trout Unlimited, The U.S. Forest Service, and dozens of local environmental and civic groups have chipped in tens of thousands of dollars toward streambed restoration efforts on Nash Stream; trout habitat is being improved by putting logs, root balls, and large boulders back into the sterile channel.

There's a paradox and a silver lining in that last line. Both Kirn and Carrier point out that in areas that weren't catastrophically damaged, the floods associated with Irene could help trout populations in the long run. Floodwaters can scour stream bottoms and enhance spawning areas, as cleaner gravel equates to higher hatch rates. And as the downed trees and debris become incorporated into the stream channel, the surviving trout will flock to the new structures. While it's disheartening to consider the short-term mortality, a flood of this magnitude is a great example of nature's penchant for regeneration through violence. Like a forest fire wiping the slate clean and allowing a pitch pine forest to start all over again, so does a flood rejuvenate a river.

Kirn says that whatever the horror of Irene, the fish and freshwater invertebrates will bounce back. "New England's a rough place to live for any fish," said Kirn. "You've got anchor ice and ice jams to contend with in winter; floods every spring; heat and low flow in the summer. But the fish have adapted to it. They take a hit and come back."

# Flat Stanley and the Centipede

Declan McCabe

Biologists sometimes field questions about a "huge scary bug" that appeared in someone's home or, worse yet, on their person. Most turn out to be benign organisms that ended up in the wrong place. For me, the most common questions come in July, when male dobsonflies emerge from the Winooski River and often end up crashing into windows on the Saint Michael's College campus where I teach. The males have impressive mandibles that look scary but are harmless to people.

Recently, however, one of these bug questions did actually involve something dangerous. One morning I received a call from a friend and grade school teacher, who explained that she had managed to corral a very large and intimidating centipede in a plastic container at her school. I immediately emailed her a photograph of a house centipede, fully expecting that to be the end of the discussion. House centipedes commonly attract the attention of teachers and homeowners. They frequently get trapped in the sink at my children's school, and I discreetly liberate them so that they can eat real pests. However, in this case, "house centipede" was not the correct answer. I asked if the arthropod was slow moving and dark, thinking that perhaps she had found a stranded hellgrammite. No, she said, it was fast.

This was getting interesting!

My friend described a centipede that was black and orange at the front, with a forked "tail" and yellow legs. Its most surprising feature was its size, a full six inches long. At this point, I asked for a photograph because the insect sounded like nothing I had encountered in Vermont. From the photograph, I determined that it was most likely a giant desert centipede (*Scolopendra heros*). That settled the first question, but left still many others unanswered. The school principal wanted to know if the centipede was dangerous. Were there likely to be more lurking about? Should he shut down the classroom? How does a desert centipede end up in Vermont?

I reassured them that it was unlikely to find even one such centipede in Vermont (and then less reassuringly suggested that, because one was found, they keep their eyes open). I informed the state entomologist and sent him photographs. I learned that desert centipedes give particularly nasty bites. In some cases, they can cause renal failure and even death. While death by centipede isn't a common way to go, even in the desert, this species was certainly due some respect.

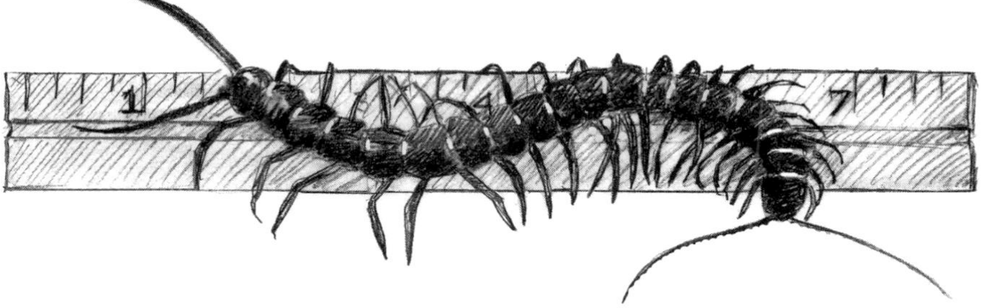

I guessed that the centipede may have come up from the desert southwest in packaging material, or perhaps through the pet trade. The truth was more surprising.

The school in question, like many Vermont schools, uses a children's book called *Flat Stanley* to combine reading skills with art, geography, and just plain fun. Because Stanley is flat, he can be mailed in an envelope, and many children in schools across the world make their own Flat Stanleys and send them to friends in other places. Their friends photograph Stanley in interesting locations and return him along with local souvenirs. When my son did this, we sent Stanley to Ireland, Cyprus, and Australia.

Stanley was sent by my friend's students to an aunt in Texas, and she mailed him back with Texas souvenirs. The package included a map of Texas, a length of rope representing the horn span of a Texas longhorn, a piece of prickly pear cactus, and a Ziploc bag with a hole chewed in the corner labeled, "DO NOT TOUCH – CENTIPEDE."

Why one sends a dangerous centipede (or any centipede) through the mail is a mystery, but it certainly happened. While I can't imagine that this centipede would establish in Vermont even if dozens were sent, it underscores the continuing need to educate the public about the dangers of moving species to new locations. On a positive note, the school has added the now dead, preserved centipede to its invertebrate collection for classroom use. I think that speaks very well for the school that the students will learn valuable lessons from Flat Stanley's travel companion. Perhaps it will inspire some budding entomologists?

*This essay was adapted from an article originally published in a newsletter of the Vermont Entomological Society: vermontinsects.org*

# Cattails: Nature's Supermarket

TIFFANY SOUKUP

Recently, I spent three months exploring East Africa, traveling through 10 different countries and covering 8,077 miles. I was continuously impressed with how much local guides knew about their surroundings, in particular the human uses of various plants. In some instances we could not walk more than 10 feet without stopping to learn about another plant and all the ways it could save your life.

This experience made me curious about plants in my own backyard. A quick skim of foraging articles on the Internet revealed that cattails, with their various edible parts, are often referred to as "nature's supermarket." I work at Seyon Lodge in Groton, Vermont, which is a stone's throw from Noyes Pond. I was thrilled to learn that I had a 40-acre produce section right outside my back door.

My first attempt at harvesting cattails was inauspicious. Shovel in hand and wearing flip flops, I jumped into the pond – and discovered that flip flops are not the best footwear for moving around in deep mud. Digging up a cattail also proved more difficult than expected. I continued to hit rocks and thick mud with my shovel. I wrenched, pried, and finally – using all of my body leverage – released what I believed to be a cattail root system from the murky water. I hurried back to the lodge, took pictures of my trophy, and then rinsed it off for careful examination. It was the red tinge inside of the roots that made me stop from going any farther. I had read that if any color other than white is visible inside the root, the plant should not be eaten. What I had pulled was yellow flag iris, which is toxic. With pond water squishing in my flip flops, I realized I needed to do more research before I started frying up foraged food.

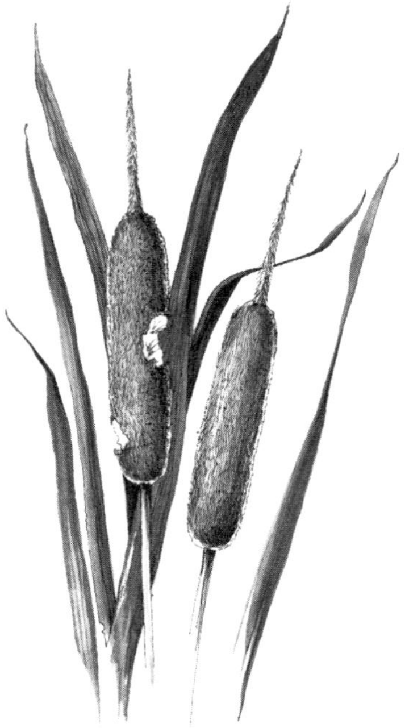

So I began reading everything I could on cattails. The most common native cattail that grows in our region is the broad leaf, *Typha latifolia*. Cattails are a true survival food, as nearly all of the plant can be eaten and they are found almost everywhere in North America except the Arctic. Their pollen is high in protein and vitamin A and the roots are an excellent source of starch. The plants also have other traditional uses. There's a record of the Chippewa tribe using the plant to make toys for their children. Cattail seed heads contain downy mounds, similar to the silk in milkweed pods. Some Native American cultures were reputed to use this material in diapers, to pack wounds, and also for bedding, clothing, and insulation.

Aside from their utility to humans, cattails play an important role in the food web, supporting many other organisms. Any sizable area of cattails is likely to host muskrats. If muskrats are around, you should also be on the lookout for their chief predator, the mink. I saw one of these small weasels in the cattails last fall. In the spring, insects that live in and on the cattails provide food for migratory birds. The plants also provide nesting habitat for many marsh birds, including red-winged blackbirds, swamp sparrows, and American bitterns.

By the time that I made my second harvest attempt, I was much better informed. I left the shovel and flip flops at the house. This time, I was after younger cattail stalks, as well as the roots. Standing barefoot in ankle-deep water, I pulled on a stalk, and easily detached it from its base. I slid my hand down a different stalk, submerging my arm into the water. I dug my fingers into the plant's base in the mud and, with a tug, found myself holding a hairy, white root with the stalk still attached. Ten minutes later I had collected enough for a meal.

Back at the lodge, I peeled the long stalks, revealing a white, slightly firm inside. I trimmed the stalks in a similar way I would prepare asparagus. After rinsing and chopping, I threw them in a pan with some butter, salt, and pepper. They were delicious, with a texture similar to an onion.

For a separate meal, I tried out one of the roots. I cut it in half lengthwise, exposing the inner, white starchy part. I sautéed it, adding a splash of water at the end. After cooking I pulled away the dense, white insides, hollowing out the root like a canoe. These strips were also very tasty.

I took a small amount of satisfaction in my accomplishment of not eating any poisonous plants. And my experience with cattails only deepened my admiration and respect for the East African guides. I am not sure if there is any better gift we can give each other than the motivation to better ourselves and seek knowledge.

# Poison Ivy on the March

NED SWANBERG

"Leaves of three, let it be." What elementary school child doesn't know this couplet about one of the most dreaded plants in our New England landscape, poison ivy? At this time of year, the three green leaves start turning shades of yellow and red, joining in the fall foliage show.

Many of us still remember our first, itchy encounter with *Toxicodendron radicans*. Like its close relatives, poison oak and poison sumac, the plant is distinguished by the powerful skin irritant urushiol. Lacking thorns or tough woody tissue, poison ivy tries to defend itself from its many predators (primarily beetles, caterpillars, and slugs) by using this chemical irritant. Deer, however, are undeterred by urushiol and include poison ivy in their long menu of suitable foods.

Poison ivy is primarily a southern species, where it co-exists with poison oak and poison sumac. In New England, the climate is too harsh for poison oak (and poison sumac only hangs on in the depths of shrubby swamps), but not for poison ivy, which is abundant in Connecticut and along the coast. Farther north, in New Hampshire and Vermont, the plant grows primarily in the bottoms of the major valleys. As you move inland and uphill from these valleys, the harsher climate limits the plant's growth, and poison ivy becomes harder to find.

In the southeastern U.S., poison ivy grows as a vine on trees, sometimes reaching three inches in diameter. As the trees grow, the ivy grows too, clinging to the trunk with tiny hairs and maintaining access to light while not having to waste energy on a strong, supportive stem.

In our climate, however, the plant does not survive the winter without the protection of snow cover, so poison ivy has adapted to grow as a low plant. It needs plenty of light, so it thrives by the sides of roads, where roadside mowing removes its woodier competitors. Healthy plants might grow to a foot in height at the edges of fields. On an old stump or other fertile spot, it might grow to four feet, though seldom more.



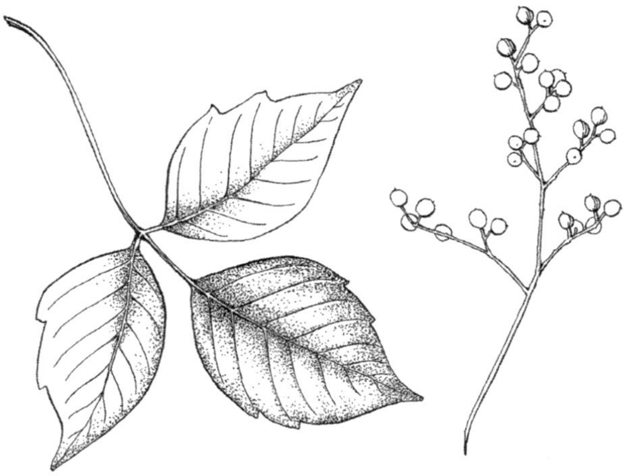

Up to 80 percent of humans are sensitive to the urushiol in poison ivy. This colorless compound is not lurking on the leaf faces themselves but rather in the sap. "Urushi" is the Japanese name for lacquer, which is made from the sap of the "urushi ki" plant, a Toxicodendron species in Asia. Urushiol passes through the skin over the course of a day or two before triggering the dermatitis. The itchy, sometimes blistering rash may last for weeks thereafter.

What should you do if you have a close encounter with poison ivy? Remove the sap from your skin immediately, since time is of the essence. After only 10 minutes, 50 percent of the urushiol has been absorbed into your skin. After an hour, it's there for good. Urushiol degrades in cool water, so rinsing in a cold stream can help. So does mashing up a poultice of juicy jewelweed stems, which can often be found growing nearby.

Poison ivy prefers warm growing conditions, and the climate of New Hampshire and Vermont is becoming warmer. This alone would lead to the plant's spread locally, but scientists at Duke University recently discovered another factor working in poison ivy's favor: the increasing concentration of carbon dioxide in the atmosphere – a result of burning fossil fuel – disproportionally favors the growth of vines. Whereas most plants are limited by a lack of nitrogen or phosphorus or potassium (the N-P-K found in commercial fertilizer), some vines are limited by $CO_2$. As we continue to burn fossil fuel, the conditions for poison ivy are steadily improving.

The Duke researchers moved the clock ahead to the estimated amount of carbon dioxide that will be in the atmosphere of 2050: 570 parts per million. At this concentration of $CO_2$, poison ivy grew twice as fast as it does today, at 380 parts per million. In addition, the plant produced a higher percentage of unsaturated urushiol, the type that is more apt to cause dermatitis. According to this study, along the roadsides of the future, there will be more poison ivy, and it will be more potent.

Poison ivy is not without its redeeming qualities, at least in the North Woods. Come winter, our northern forests provide relatively poor pickings for wildlife. Where they are available, poison ivy berries are rich in fats, and the berries can persist on the plant through the season. *Toxicodendron radicans* berries are eaten by bluebirds, myrtle warblers, and 26 other local bird species. The birds, in turn, disperse the seeds as they migrate. Poison ivy, like cherry, shadblow, grape, oak, and many other species, is part of the dynamic bird-dispersed landscape of our region.

# Staycation Geese and Southbound Juncos? It's Complicated.

Carolyn Lorié

This has always been my perception of bird migration in the fall: the days grow short and cool and then, one day, I notice a v-shaped caravan of Canada geese flying southward. Then another and another. Within a few weeks of that first sighting, I hear their melancholy call one final time for the season. Then they, and all the summer birds, are gone. It's a mass exodus for warmer climes, over and done in the blink of an eye and long before the snow flies.

But what of the geese on the unfrozen mill ponds in January? Or the robins at the birdfeeder in December? It turns out that the process of migration is much longer and less predictable than my cursory observations had led me to believe. First of all, for some species fall migration begins long before the first ears of corn are ready to be picked. Take, for example, the yellow warbler, whose massive breeding range extends from parts of Mexico to Newfoundland and into Alaska. It is among the earliest songbirds to arrive in the spring and among the first to embark on the return journey.

According to Andrew Farnsworth, a research associate with the Cornell Lab for Ornithology, birders in northern New England may notice yellow warblers from the end of April to as late as mid-September, and conclude that those birds stay for all the months in between. But that's not what is going on.

SEP

The birds that settle in our area in the spring start the breeding cycle earlier than those that go on to nest in northern Canada or Alaska. By late June or early July, the newly hatched yellow warblers of our region fledge. They and their parents start their journey back to Central and South America. But their departure does not mean the absence of the species in our area, as yellow warblers from more northern areas, and therefore later breeding cycles, will begin passing through. We get the pleasure of the yellow warblers' presence from April through September – just not the same individual birds.

Some birds, like dark-eyed juncos, we see year-round, giving the impression that they are non-migratory. But again, this is not entirely accurate, said Farnsworth. Some juncos may stay put in northern New England right through winter. But those tend to be the birds that are behaviorally dominant – that is, they are able to secure a desirable territory, keeping competition at bay. Less dominant birds may be forced to migrate to southern regions in search of food and their departure may take place as late as December.

While fall and winter mark the departure of many birds from our region, it can also be a time of arrival for a few species. Among them are common redpolls, which make their home in the arctic tundra and boreal forests, and pine siskins, which tend to be year-round residents in the more southern areas of Canada and mountainous regions in the western United States. These birds are known as irruptive migrants, meaning they will move only if food in their usual territory becomes scarce. So you may see large flocks of common redpolls at your feeder one year, but not a single redpoll the following year.

This fall, as I watch a flock of Canada geese fade from sight, I will know that it is neither the beginning nor the end of the season's migration. It turns out that birds' seasonal movement is a long and complex process that varies bird by bird, and from one year to the next.

# Goldenrod: The Everything, Everywhere Flower

JOE RANKIN

Where I live, the three warmer seasons are colored gold. In mid-May, the fields are covered with dandelions. Then come the buttercups, which turn the landscape into a real-life Monet painting. Now, as summer turns to fall, goldenrods.

These members of the aster family love old fields, and even in active fields where hay is harvested, they stand tall around the edges, glowing in the sun as the days grow shorter and the wind picks up bite. You'll find them along dirt roads, on highway medians, and edging the forest. Because they're not shy, goldenrods get blamed for causing allergies. In fact, the culprit is generally ragweed, whose billions of light pollen grains float on the wind. Goldenrod pollen is heavy and spread by insects – especially by my honeybees.

To a beekeeper, a good goldenrod nectar flow is nature's late-summer gift. It can help ensure that bees have enough honey stores to survive the winter and, in a good year, provide the beekeeper with some to put on his toast. Goldenrod nectar ripening in a hive gives off a strong odor. The honey is darker than the lighter summer honeys and tends to crystallize rapidly. Interestingly, not all goldenrods are equally attractive to bees.

Bumblebees, beetles, flies, moths, and butterflies also feast on goldenrod, and in turn, wasps, beetles, spiders, and birds prey on the insects attracted to the yellow-topped stalks. There's even a goldenrod spider, named for its preference for the plant as its hunting ground.

This time of year, it seems like goldenrod can be seen just about everywhere, and it's no wonder, with 70 species in North America, 25 of which can be found in New England, according to Arthur Haines, research botanist for the New England Wild Flower Society.

The U.S. Department of Agriculture's Plant Database distribution map for goldenrod shows a completely filled-in map of the U.S. and Canada, from Baffin Island to the Virgin Islands to Hawaii. There are goldenrods that grow in the salt air on seaside dunes (seaside goldenrod), on tops of high mountains (alpine goldenrod), in arctic tundra (Rocky Mountain goldenrod), in bogs (bog goldenrod), in fields (too many species to mention). There's even one that grows in woods (wood goldenrod). There are goldenrods in Mexico and South America, Europe, and Asia, some of which are exotic invasives imported from North America.

With so many species, identifying goldenrods can be frustrating. On a recent September morning, I waded into the field across the road, armed with what I thought was a perfectly adequate wildflower guide. After 20 minutes, I figured out there were four or five different species of goldenrod in that sea of yellow, but I wasn't able to definitively identify any single one. "It's hard for people to use amateur guides to identify goldenrods," said Haines. "But if you spent an hour learning the terminology, had good optics to magnify things, and a good measurement tool, you'd walk away with a different opinion."

Solidago, goldenrod's Latin name, means "becoming whole," a reference to the plant's numerous medicinal uses. Native Americans boiled the leaves and stems to make a tonic to bathe wounds and rashes. Elsewhere, people used goldenrod to treat everything from bladder infections to kidney stones, sore throats to tuberculosis. Canada goldenrod, a common species in Vermont and New Hampshire, "is a urinary tract antiseptic and anti-inflammatory," Haines said. "It has a great role in treating urinary tract infections. It's something I have shared with a number of different people who say that it works, always, all the time." And it's easy: dry the flowers and leaves and make a tea of them.

Goldenrod was traditionally used to make a beautiful yellow dye. The leaves also contain rubber and there were once efforts (by Thomas Edison, no less) to breed goldenrod for rubber production. It never went anywhere because the rubber quality wasn't good enough for tires.

Gardeners are keen on goldenrod, as well. Flower hybridizers have taken the native goldenrods and created new cultivars with showier blooms. They are, however, all yellow. A plus for the northern gardener: they're hardy. A minus: some cultivars can take over your flower bed faster than you can spell rhizome, which is not surprising considering the fact that goldenrods are colonizers of disturbed areas, and a nicely tilled garden is just that.

While they're an aggressive plant, it's comforting to know that unlike many of the exotics you see blooming in a fallow field, goldenrod was here long before we were. "I can't think of a single non-native goldenrod that grows in this part of the world," Haines told me.

For a fun autumn activity related to this essay, turn to page 214.

# october

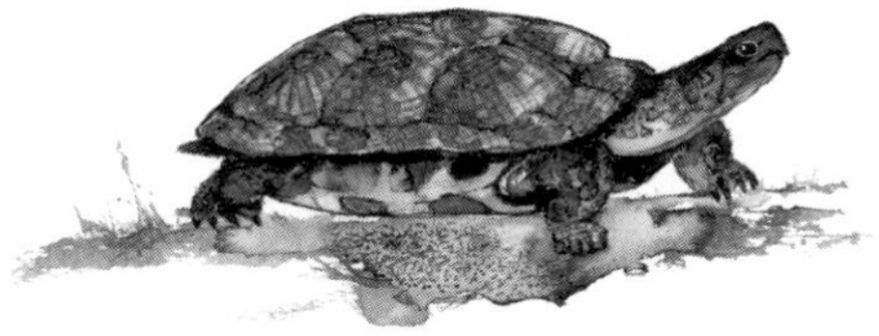



## 1 first week

Sparrow migration is well underway, with white-crowned, song, chipping, white-throated, savannah, swamp, tree, and fox sparrows all on the move.

Wood turtles return to streams, rivers, and ponds to mate before hibernating in undercut banks and root masses.

Hard up birds may be eating jack-in-the-pulpit berries, generally considered to be a low quality wildlife food.

Damselflies and dragonflies may still be flying around, mating, and laying eggs.

## 2 second week

Sugar maples at peak color.

Apple cider pressing is in full swing.

It's skunks that leave those small conical holes in the lawn while doing pest control for you: beetle larvae are a skunk favorite.

Halloween lady beetles are seeking shelter in houses. Each one has consumed about 300 aphids during its larval stage, but these newcomers might be outcompeting native lady beetles.

Evergreen woodferns are still bright green and will stay green all winter.

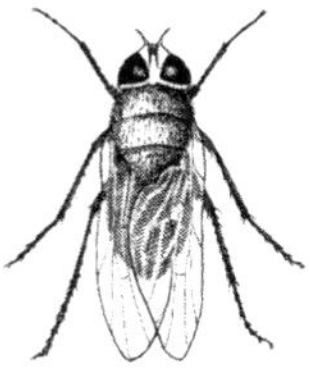



## third week

Orionid meteor shower peaks around this time. This shower is produced by the dust left by Halley's Comet and is best seen after midnight.

Most killdeer leave during the last half of October. They will begin to return in March.

The nests of paper wasps become more visible now that the leaves have fallen. These large structures are begun by a single female (the queen) and enlarged over the summer by her many offspring.

Flocks of juncos arrive from the north.

## fourth week

Snow geese are migrating, often in huge flocks.

At least two species of cluster fly are from Europe. They are experts at squeezing through tiny spaces to get into your house.

Fishers are eating apples, berries, and nuts now. Their diet does not consist entirely of small mammals and house cats.

Apple eaters include red and gray fox, eastern coyote, fisher, black bear, raccoon, opossum, whitetail deer, porcupine, beaver, wild turkey, and pine grosbeak.

# Chipmunk Game Theory 101

Elise Tillinghast

Two chipmunks vie for seeds on our front lawn. One lives directly underneath the bird feeder. Another hails from the far side of the house, address unknown.

The chipmunks appear identical to me: same size, same stripes. Same interests, namely seed hoarding, aggressive chittering, jumping into the bushes and back out again, and brazen stiff-tailed standoffs with the dog.

However, some aspects of these chipmunks' behavior are probably distinctive. Experiments have demonstrated that a chipmunk's choosiness about what food it collects, how fully it stuffs its cheek pouches, and even how quickly it stuffs food in there, all relate to the distance between a foraging site and a home burrow.

The eastern chipmunk, *Tamias striatus*, is a central-place forager. This means that, similar to the beaver and the honeybee, the chipmunk carries food back to a central location. This time of year, that location is the chipmunk's winter burrow. It's an impressive feat of earthworks that includes a bedroom, bathroom, several tunnels to the surface, and multiple larders.

In late autumn, the chipmunk retreats to its bedroom, tucks its tail over its nose, and sinks into a deep sleep. However, unlike many other hibernating mammals, the chipmunk doesn't sleep the winter away. Because it lacks fat reserves, it has to wake up frequently to feed.

In other words, chipmunks have good cause for their hoarding obsession. But their intense foraging activity has a cost. The time and energy that a chipmunk spends obtaining and hauling food from a particular site, be it a birdfeeder or a patch of forest floor, represent precious calories invested and other opportunities sacrificed. As established food sites are depleted, chipmunks have to go out and look for new ones, and this is an energy gamble. Long distance foraging may offer access to more desirable food sites, but it requires more travel time and increases the risk of predation.

Then there is the "loading curve" consideration. In general, the more food a chipmunk stuffs in its cheek pouches, the slower its subsequent stuffing, and therefore the greater its overall risk of predation. Nor is every food item created equal. In addition to issues of durability and nutritive value, some food is simply easier to harvest and stuff than other food.

As if all these factors weren't enough to worry about, chipmunks have another problem to manage: other chipmunks. Chipmunk territories average about 5,000 square meters (a little more than an acre) and they overlap. This means that rivals lurk nearby, poised to hoover up food at a forage site, or even steal from undefended burrows.

So how does all this play out underneath the bird feeder?

Fortunately for the inquisitive, there has been extensive research in central-place foraging over the past few decades, and the chipmunk is the protagonist of numerous scholarly papers. Some of these veer to the unintentionally funny. My favorite example, a paper out of the Université du Québec, describes an experiment assessing chipmunk reactions to sunflower seeds that had toothpicks stuck to their shells with Advanced Formula Instant Krazy Glue.

Out of all this research emerges what might be called the guiding rule of chipmunk foraging: chipmunks have evolved to be energy maximizers. They seek to strike the optimal balance between the energy gain per cheek pouch load and the highest possible number of trips back to the burrow. In the absence of other variables, a chipmunk that is near its burrow will have smaller pouch loads and make more frequent trips than a chipmunk from a distant burrow, which will stuff its cheeks full before heading back home.

Of course, chipmunks' lives teem with other variables, and studies show that chipmunk behavior adapts to take many of them into account. Here are some basics from Chipmunk Game Theory 101.

If another chipmunk is making a lot of noise, it might be fussing at you, but it also may have spotted a hawk or a weasel. Slow down pouch stuffing and look out for predators. If food is low quality and far from home, seek another foraging site. If a site has a dwindling supply of food, or if the food requires extensive handling time (i.e., seeds covered with toothpicks and Krazy Glue), take time during your return trip to explore alternative sites. If a dominant chipmunk temporarily vacates a food site, spend more time there and stuff all you can. If another chipmunk is at the food site, slow down stuffing and keep an eye on them. If a subordinate chipmunk is intruding on your territory, chase them. Sure, it will cost you energy, but it will cost them energy too, and maybe they won't come back.

Of course, it's easy to imagine more factors: weather, steepness of terrain between burrow and foraging site...how about pouch fatigue? My small primate brain boggles at the complexities. It's enough to make me want to chitter aggressively, jump into the bushes, and jump back out again.

# Woolly Bears: Forecast Flops?

Barbara Mackay

Autumn is coming to a close. The brilliant fall foliage is past peak, if not already layered in the compost bin. The last geese are honking their way toward winter homes. Predictions are proffered (sometimes cheerfully, mostly not) for how cold and snowy this year's winter will be.

Sources for seasonal predictions vary. *The Farmers' Almanac* and traditional old wives' tales are often cited. How soon those geese head south, for example, is supposed to indicate how difficult winter will be. We trust these bits of folklore because they often have a scientific basis and seem to work. (Research is advised, however; never assume that country wisdom is reliable enough to calculate, say, your heating oil pre-buy needs.)

Sometimes the cuteness factor plays a role in our willingness to believe. Take the woolly bear caterpillar, whose fuzziness often tempts people to pick it up, and coincidentally, to discover that the bristles, called setae, are actually stiff and hard, not soft and cuddly. It is on the prowl in late fall, crossing lawns, logs, and roads. According to tradition, the wider the rusty-orange band around its middle, the milder the coming winter. The relative size of its two black sections is also supposed to have meteorological significance. If the front one is larger than the back one, the beginning of winter will supposedly have colder temperatures than the end of winter, and vice versa.

In fact, woolly bears are better predictors of the past spring and summer than the coming winter. Like all caterpillars, the woolly bear goes through several stages of development, called instars. Each instar is a period of steady eating and growth, culminating in the shedding of now-too-tight skin. During each molt, some of the black-bristled segments are replaced with orange ones. Fall is well under way by the fifth or sixth instar, just when we begin comparing the forecast and the caterpillar.

What this means is that the ratio of black to orange actually depends on the caterpillar's age and developmental stage. Very young woolly bears are almost entirely dark. If spring came early, the woolly bear will have had additional time for growth, resulting in a wide orange band by fall. On the other hand, lack of rain in the spring and summer may limit its food supply (dandelions, grass, clover, nettles, and birches are preferred) and delay growth. Looking at a stressed, spring-size caterpillar in November may tell you something about the previous months' weather conditions, but won't be of much help with the question of



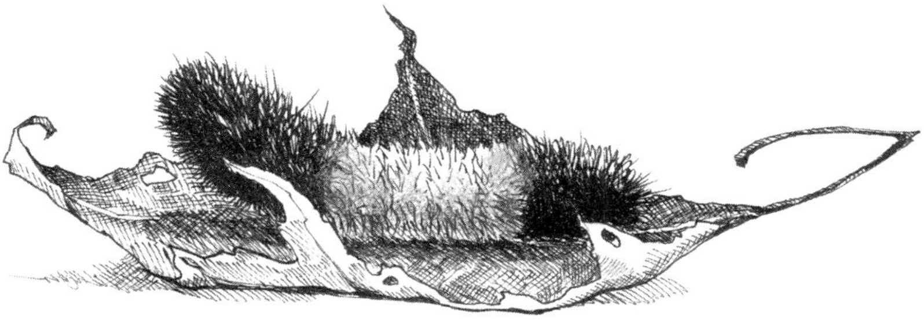

whether your wood pile needs supplementing. As autumn edges closer to winter, these caterpillars seek out a place to hibernate. They may wander surprisingly far in their quest. Choice spots are under leaf litter, in a wood pile, even behind loose bark. Here they are out of the elements, but by no means protected from freezing. In fact, they must freeze in order to survive the winter.

Like frogs, woolly bears make a substance that acts like antifreeze. As the late autumn temperatures drop, the caterpillar gradually fills with glycerol. This viscous substance basically prevents organs and sensitive tissues from getting freezer burn. The setae also contribute to the winterizing process by drawing water out of the caterpillar's body. Ice crystals form harmlessly on the bristles instead of inside the body, where cells critical to life reside and where ice crystals could prove deadly. Eventually, only the interior of each cell remains unfrozen, safely surrounded by cold-tolerant glycerol.

With ice on the outside and glycerol on the inside, the caterpillar is ready to endure a long period of cold weather. This period of arctic diapause is so critical that a mild winter can spell doom for woolly bears. (So, too, can soft-hearted but misinformed "protectors" who relocate one to the garage, "so the poor caterpillar won't freeze to death.") Sheltered from snow and wind by its leaf or log shelter, the frozen caterpillar can withstand temperatures well below zero.

Looking like a crispy tortellini, it lies as though lifeless until spring temperatures warm it up. Once it thaws, it resumes ravenous eating as though never interrupted. After a few days of gorging on tender greens, the banded larva finds a site to spin a cocoon with its bristles and silk. Woodpiles are again favorite spots, but any secure surface will do. Every year I find four or five inside an empty wren house.

A miraculous transformation takes place inside the cocoon over the next one to two weeks. Then, one day, a delicate yellow-orange Isabella tiger moth (*Pyrrharctia isabella*) emerges without warning. You're not likely to see it unless you have a porch light, however, as it is both nocturnal and short-lived. It will mate, lay eggs, and die within a matter of weeks, leaving its offspring to carry on the role of pretend prognosticators.

For a fun autumn activity related to this essay, turn to page 212.

# Mast Mysteries

Dave Mance III

Nature writers spend a lot of time celebrating the unknowns in the natural world, those little reminders that we're not as smart as we think we are. It's an especially resonant message if you're sitting at the kitchen table, surrounded by the inorganic trappings of domestic life – in other words when you need a kick in the behind – but it's harder to appreciate when you're afield, looking at a pile of beech nuts that look viable until you undress them and find that they have no nut meat – they're like ghost nuts – and your three-year-old niece is saying *why? why? why?*, and you're saying *dun-no, dun-no, dun-no*, sort of like a crow and a chickadee squawking back and forth.

Hard mast, the term used to refer to the nuts that wild trees produce, is humbling this way. We know that, generally speaking, trees require a lot of energy to produce nuts, and so a tree won't produce them every year. The books say every two or three years for beech nuts and three to seven years for oaks, but take it all with a grain of salt. We had back-to-back good acorn years around our deer camp in southern Vermont in 2010 and 2011 but struck out in 2012 and 2013; we had a good beech mast year in 2010 but not in the three years that followed.

There are advantages, from a tree's perspective, to being unpredictable. Abundant years followed by lean years keep seed predators in check. (Biologists call this predator satiation.) In a good year, the woods are flooded with nuts – more than any squirrel or mouse can eat. The next fall, when rodent populations are high thanks to all the easy living, the trees take the year off and the surplus rodents starve.

Beech trees and rodents share the strategy of flooding an area with offspring in a way that ensures species survival, even if large numbers of individuals perish. Bears, also voracious consumers of beech nuts, have a more sophisticated reproductive strategy. In good mast years, they gorge themselves and convert the extra protein into bear cubs. In a bad year, a female bear's body might decide in December that she's not fat enough to give birth and will then abort the fertilized embryo she's been carrying since June.

We know that mast production often happens on a region-wide basis: most of the beech trees in a forest will make nuts on the same year, though we don't really know how they communicate this plan to one another. Maybe there's some direct chemical signal – molecules that float through the air – or maybe a mycorrhizal signal gets passed underground via the fungal communities that tree roots share. Maybe the trees get cues from the environment. A warm April, say, might cause the trees to invest resources into reproduction that year, while in a cool year they will invest in growth. This phenomenon, called the Moran effect, has led some to hypothesize that as global temperatures rise, mast years will become more frequent, which could lead to an overabundance of rodents that could throw whole ecosystems out of whack.

As for the fake nuts you might find around your deer stand this year, beech expert Dave Houston confirmed for me that these were nuts that never got pollinated. Beech is wind-pollinated, which leaves them susceptible to the vagaries of spring weather. A lot of rain might mean a bad pollination year. Also, the tree has relatively heavy pollen that doesn't disperse particularly well, which might mean that dense stands of beech will have more pollinated nuts than individual beech trees growing among other hardwoods. On any mast year there will be a mix of pollinated and unpollinated nuts, though pollination rates vary widely.

Why would a tree put energy into making a fake nut? Tom Vogelmann, a plant biologist at the University of Vermont, says that the empty husks are made of carbon, which is a relatively cheap commodity to a tree. The actual nut is the expensive item, as it uses up precious nitrogen to make protein. Since it doesn't take that much effort to make an empty nut, maybe the answer is that, like a female bear, going part-way gives the tree the ability to assess its resources and make a last-minute decision about whether or not to make (a couple thousand) offspring.

# The Halloween Ladybeetle: Your Uninvited House Guest

VIRGINIA BARLOW

In the old days, ladybeetles (or ladybugs) used to "flyaway home" to their children, as per the old nursery rhyme. Now one species, the Halloween ladybeetle, is instead flying into our homes in droves, where its bad odor and habit of falling into cups of coffee have contributed to its dramatic fall from grace.

The ladybeetle family includes many cute and shiny beetles – they're usually bright orange or red, with some black and white thrown in for contrast. As a group, they specialize in consuming agricultural pests, especially aphids, and they don't sting or bite. These attributes and the fact that there are so many of them – about 5,000 species worldwide and around 475 in the U.S. – have contributed to making ladybeetles among the most beloved of all the insects.

Properly called the multicolored Asian ladybeetle, this little insect has so many other names that in the U.K. it's sometimes known as "the many-named ladybird." (What we know as "ladybugs" are called "ladybirds" in other English speaking countries.)

In truth, they are not bugs or birds; they are beetles. This species is unusually varied in appearance, ranging from pale orange to deep red, occasionally with no spots and sometimes with as many as 16 spots, but they do have a distinctive feature: between the wings and the head, on the prothorax, are markings in black and white that can be read as a "W" or an "M."

In 1888, an Australian species of ladybeetle was brought to America to control a scale insect that threatened the California citrus crop; this was the very first recorded case of a predatory insect being deliberately imported to the U.S. The release was enormously successful, so much so that it spurred the widespread and haphazard release of various ladybeetle species all around the world.

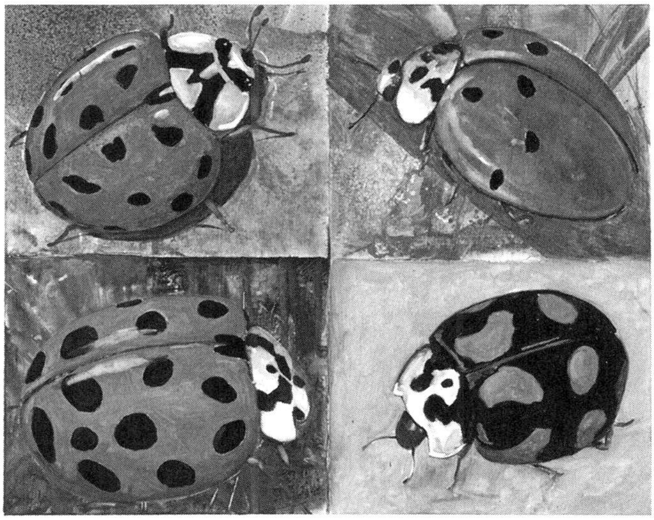

OCT

The Halloween ladybeetle, native to eastern and central Asia, soon became a favorite for biological control projects because it eats a wide variety of insects in the egg and larval form. Since its introduction the species has devoured aphid species that feed on soybeans, roses, strawberries, red pines, balsam firs, and pecans; it has also been found to feed on red pine scale and pine bark adelgid. The beetle is a voracious predator and a friendly alternative to toxic pesticides; unfortunately, its indiscriminating palette has gotten it into deep trouble. The very trait that enabled it to colonize most of the world has also inspired a backlash.

After it has done in the aphids, both adult and larval Halloween ladybeetles move on to feed upon the larvae of other ladybeetle species and the eggs and larvae of many other kinds of insects. In some studies, it has been shown to have an adverse effect on monarch butterfly populations, and in several states a decline of native ladybeetles was documented not long after the Halloweens arrived. Winemakers really hate Halloween ladybeetles because not only do they eat the grapes, but those that get harvested with the grapes produce a most unpleasant flavor in the wine. This ladybeetle has recently made its way to the U.K., and some scientists believe that 1,000 native species there could disappear if the new beetle flourishes.

Halloween ladybeetles are a bit larger than most of our native species, which may help explain their success. Depending on the size of the aphid, a ladybeetle will eat from 90 to 370 aphids during its larval stage. The beetles usually produce two broods each year, and in the laboratory, where it's possible to count, females each laid an average of 1,600 eggs. All ladybeetles use defensive chemicals in their hemolymph (circulatory fluid) to discourage would-be predators, but the Halloween has these foul-tasting and -smelling compounds in higher concentrations than its relatives. Nobody eats them or their eggs or their larvae. In winter, they maximize the effectiveness of these deterrents by glomming together in groups. They vary in behavior and morphology as well as in appearance, which allows them to adapt to changing environmental conditions.

Many introductions of the beetle have been made since 1916, but the beetle population showed no sign of taking off until 1988. No one knows what might have triggered the population explosion.

Once a beetle population becomes established, the rapidity with which it colonizes new territory is astounding. In 2004, only one of these beetles was found in Switzerland, and none were found in 2005. Yet, by 2006, it was established in 10 cantons; in 2007, in some areas, it was the most abundant ladybeetle on deciduous trees; and in 2008, it was more abundant than all the native ladybeetles added together.

Now the Halloween ladybeetle is finding food in 24 countries in Europe and has been seen checking the menu in South America, South Africa, and Egypt. Though it has been in the U.S. for almost 100 years, it was just over 20 years ago that the population explosion came to people's attention here.

# What (F)lies Beneath: Avian Bloodsuckers

MEGHAN OLIVER

When you find a bird feather in the woods and stoop to pick it up, does your mother's voice echo in your brain? Can you hear her say, "birds have lice, don't pick that up?" Mom was mostly right. Birds can have lice (though you won't catch lice from a bird). But what Mom probably didn't know is that birds have something far creepier lurking in their feathers. It's six-legged, leathery, and flat. And it sucks blood.

The good news? It does not want to suck *your* blood.

Avian hippoboscid flies – also called flat flies and louse flies – survive on bird blood. Estimates vary for the number of different species in our region, but there are likely more than 10, fewer than 20.

These flies are ectoparasites, living *on* the bird rather than in it. Alan Graham, Vermont's state entomologist, has an extensive collection of avian and other louse fly species, and he has identified a diversity of bird hosts, ranging from northern flickers to song sparrows, barred owls to blackpoll warblers. While Graham said larger birds often host larger species of flies, this is not always the case. Birds may be infested with more than one hippoboscid species at a time.

To the casual observer, a hippoboscid looks a lot like a common house fly, except flatter, as if someone had stepped on them. This low profile helps them scuttle sideways, crab-like, over and under feathers. They have claws that help them cling to feathers and a special needle-like proboscis protected by mouth parts on either side that unfold at mealtime. When a fly is ready to dine, it pierces the bird's skin with its proboscis and slurps up a meal.

Catherine Greenleaf, director of Saint Francis Wild Bird Hospital in Lyme, New Hampshire, finds hippoboscids most commonly on birds of prey (eagles, hawks, owls), particularly those at death's door. She described the insects as grim reapers and vampires. In her experience, emaciated birds covered in hippoboscid flies almost always test positive for anemia.

Greenleaf also described another unpleasant feature of these flies – their penchant for flying off bird patients and directly into the hair of rehabilitators, where they don't bite but are "really gross" and "very hard to catch."

While Alan Graham couldn't give an estimate as to the lifespan of these flies, he said he's collected specimens in winter, suggesting they can survive the cold. Living against the skin of a warm-blooded bird with the extra protection of insulating feathers helps keep them alive.

As for offspring, the flies have one of the lowest reproduction rates in the insect world. According to *The Manual of the Neartic Diptera*, hippoboscid females may produce just seven to eight offspring in a lifetime. Whereas the common housefly may lay clusters of thousands of eggs at a time, with hippoboscids, only one egg is produced, and it's not laid at all. A single larva hatches within the mother louse fly's uterus. In this protected environment, the young insect completes its larval development. The female lays the larva, which pupates. When the adult fly emerges from the pupa it immediately begins to hunt.

One theory for these flies' low reproductive rate is that a proliferation of them might eliminate host populations. John Burger, a professor of zoology at the University of New Hampshire, also suggested a limiting factor on *adult* hippoboscid numbers: sometimes, the birds bite back. "My guess," he said, "is that the life of a hippoboscid fly is quite chancy," with some being eaten by their host if the host can nip them.

So if you happen upon an injured bird, know that the avian species you're looking at may not be the only winged creature down. Louse flies may lie beneath. But take comfort in the fact that they have no interest in you. Mom's got no need to worry.

# Puff, the Magic Mushroom

MADELINE BODIN

Who left that soccer ball on the front lawn? Come on, you know it didn't just grow there.

Pretending to confuse a giant puffball mushroom with a soccer ball (or vice versa) is a well-worn joke among mushroom foragers. For the rest of us, finding out that there exists a common mushroom in Vermont and New Hampshire that frequently grows to soccer ball size sounds like more of a hidden-camera, the-joke's-on-you kind of gag.

Not only do these giant mushrooms exist, says Ari Rockland Miller, a Vermont-based mushroom foraging expert, they are edible, even delectable, early in their lifecycle, when their flesh is white and has the consistency of Styrofoam.

Giant puffballs are unusual among mushrooms because they love sun. You can find them from summer to fall on lawns, in fields, and in cemeteries. More rain generally means more mushrooms, including puffballs. Tropical Storm Irene, which arrived in August 2011 after a wet summer, unleashed a mushroom bonanza that foragers are still talking about.

By this late in autumn, most giant puffballs aren't any good for eating, but they're great for entertainment purposes. For a certain type of kid (and a certain type of adult), finding one of these round, white mushrooms when it's in its dry, papery stage is a joy. Jump on it. Kick it. Throw it at your friend. (You didn't hear that last one from me, though.) Poof. It pops open and dark "smoke" appears.

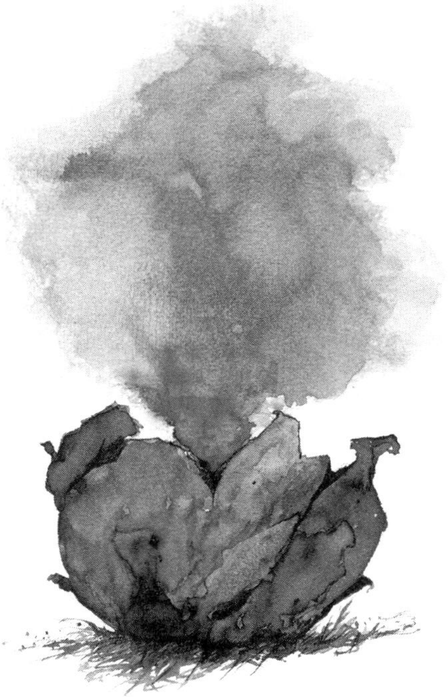

That dusty smoke is actually trillions of mushroom spores, says Rockland-Miller. As a giant puffball ages, it dries out. Its outside develops cracks (unlike other puffball species, which develop holes at their tops), and its inside fills with tiny spores. Once the cracks are large enough, the spores disperse. Although most of the spores land near the parent puffball, if the wind – or a lucky kick – sends them flying, the sky is the limit. Aerobiologists have collected fungal spores at 10,000 feet; they've even been found blowing over the Arctic.

Giant puffballs are considered one of the easiest mushrooms to identify, because once they get bigger than your fist, there is really nothing else they can be mistaken for. However, Rockland-Miller says, small puffballs can be mistaken for the young versions of some of the deadliest mushrooms around here – Amanita mushrooms, a genus that includes the death cap and the destroying angel.

There are a number of other mushrooms growing in our area that bear some resemblance to the giant puffball, at least in some of their life stages. Many of their common names are fanciful; Rockland-Miller guesses that the author of an important field guide to mushrooms made up many of these names, and they reflect his wry sense of humor. These include the skull-shaped puffball, purple-spored puffball, gem-studded puffball, and pear-shaped puffball. There is also the pigskin poison puffball, which is not a true puffball, but one of a closely related group of mushrooms called earthballs. It's brown, football-shaped, and, yes, poisonous. Another closely related group of mushrooms are the earthstars, which unfurl starfish-like enclosures from central, spore-storing balls.

Of all these species, only the giant puffballs grow to soccer ball size, or even larger. The big ones are startling enough to attract media attention. In early October of 2013, a newspaper article about some giant puffballs on a Michigan couple's front lawn appeared in newspapers around the country. In September of the same year, a giant puffball in Monkton, Vermont, made the local television news. Its owner cut it open on camera to show its foamy, white flesh – just right for eating. The puffball was roughly the size of a basketball.

As for that suspicious orb on your lawn, here's a test that works this time of year. Kick it. If it puffs out smoke, it's probably a mushroom. If it rolls, it probably belongs to your neighbor's kid.

# november

1

# first week

Monarchs begin arriving at their overwintering site in Mexico; some have travelled 3,000 miles. In March, they'll head north but will lay eggs part way home, leaving it to the next generations to get back to New England.

Luna moth cocoons, wrapped in brown leaves, have fallen to the ground.

Some golden-crowned kinglets migrate, but some are found here through the winter, which is amazing considering that they aren't much larger than a hummingbird.

# second week

2

Rattlesnake plantain (it's really an orchid) stays green all winter. The leaves are covered with a net of white veins and grow in a small rosette.

Bruce spanworm moths, also called hunter's moths, may be abundant in sugar maple stands on sunny days from mid-October through November.

Scarves of smoke rise from deer camp chimneys.

Meadow voles are still breeding.

Hooded mergansers go south just far enough to find ice-free water. Most of them have left by now.

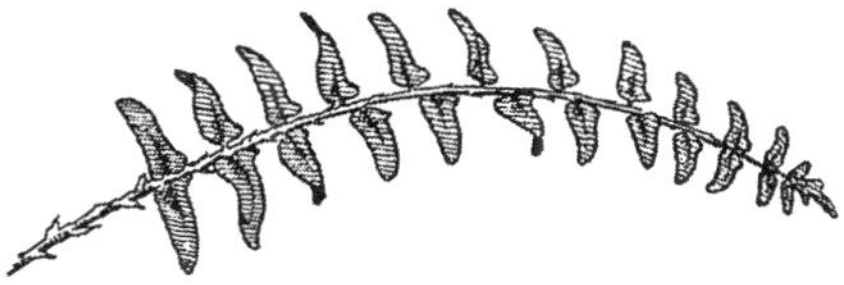



## third week

As pond ice thickens, beavers will be stuck in their lodges or below the ice till spring.

Snowshoe hares are all white by the end of November, and praying for snow.

Eastern red-backed salamanders are headed downwards.
Sometimes they use the burrows of other animals to get below the frost line.

Shagbark hickory nuts are falling from their husks.
Wood ducks and wild turkeys eat them, as do many mammals.

The last litter of deer mice is on its own.

## fourth week

Moose antlers can weigh 30 to 60 pounds and have a five-foot spread.

Falling birch seeds will travel far if blown across crusted snow.

Christmas fern stays green not just till Christmas, but till next summer. The individual pinnae are shaped like Christmas stockings – another way to remember the name.

Males of many migrating bird species don't fly as far south as the females, perhaps so they can return north earlier to claim a high-quality territory.

# Canis Soupus: The Eastern Coy-Wolf

DAVE MANCE III

As any biologist will tell you, different species of animal can't breed with one another. Well, they can, but nature has a way of jumping in and nipping such cross pollination in the bud. For example, a horse can mate with a donkey, but the resulting honkey (ok, mule) should be sterile. Cattalo (cow/buffalo crosses) produce sterile males. Whitetailed deer/blacktailed deer crosses produce sterile females that presumably have gray tails.

But as an evolutionary biology student might tell you, there always seems to be a confusing exception to these so-called rules. Around here, that exception is the eastern coyote (*Canis latrans*), a species that can freely hybridize with both dogs and wolves and produce fertile offspring.

Coyotes didn't used to live here. Historically, wolves ruled the forests in the Northeast, and coyotes were something that lived out west. Habitat loss and human exploitation wiped out the wolves in the mid-1800s, and for 100 years that was pretty much that.

But 60 or 70 years ago, a strange little wolflike creature started showing up in our region. At first, people didn't know what to make of it. It sort of looked like a western coyote, but it was about 30 percent bigger. And its color palette was all over the map. Trappers were bringing in creatures that were all black, or blond, or reddish. Some looked like German-shepherds, which led to the colloquial term coy-dog. But this new animal's skull didn't look like a dog's or a coy-dog's, it looked more like a cross between a western coyote and a wolf. Today, DNA evidence is proving that that's exactly what the eastern coyote is.

Several years ago, coyote hunters and trappers from Ohio to Maine contributed nearly 700 coyote tissue samples to a coyote genetics study led by Dr. Roland Kays at the New York State Museum. Every northeastern animal except one in the study contained a combination of wolf-like and coyote-like genes – only one sample was dog-like. What's more, the scientists were able to determine that the wolf DNA was typical of wolves from eastern Canada and the Great Lakes region. The genetic patterns in the coyotes from Ohio, however, had no wolf-like influences and closely resembled western coyotes.

By comparing the DNA analysis to historical records, Kays developed a theory that the coyotes in the Northeast arrived in two separate waves. The northern group emigrated east through Ontario, picking up wolf genes along the way. This hybridization led to larger, faster bodies and more wolf-like feeding habits. (Western coyotes focus on rabbits and rodents for the meat portion of their omnivorous diet; the eastern coyote eats more deer and fewer mice.) The second group emigrated east from Indiana through Ohio and Pennsylvania. The coyotes in the Adirondacks, Vermont, New Hampshire, and Maine trace their roots back to the northern front, while animals in western New York and Pennsylvania represent the purer western coyote strains that are moving east. In that area, the northern coyotes are mixing with the western coyotes, and with each passing breeding season, the cards are getting more and more jumbled.

Because coyotes are turning out to be such a genetic hodgepodge, the joke in mammology circles is that in deference to the gray wolf's scientific name, *Canis lupus*, the coyote should be renamed *Canis soupus*. Kays says that it's anyone's guess as to how the evolutionary history of the eastern coyote will play out. He doesn't know if the two groups recognize each other as being different. He doesn't know if one set of genes will prove more successful than the other. Maybe evolution will favor the genetics from the northern wave, as the bigger bodies make the animals better deer hunters. Or maybe the purer, smaller western-type genes that came from the south and east will prove more successful in our fragmented, increasingly suburban landscape.

One thing we are sure of is that in 60 years' time, coyotes have firmly established themselves as residents in just about every corner of the Northeast. They've also done a great job of turning conventional biological wisdom on its head.

# Now's a Good Time to Ride Off Into the Sunset

Meghan Oliver

It seems each autumn, I start noticing sunsets more. They are so pink, so orange, so bright. I've always chalked up my autumnal sunset attention to my mood shifting with the changing season; perhaps I'm feeling a little wistful at summer's end and reflecting on nature's splendor more than usual. But according to the National Oceanic and Atmospheric Administration (NOAA), the colors we see during sunsets really are more vibrant in fall and winter than they are in spring and summer – seasonal melancholia has got nothing to do with it.

The intensity of sunset and sunrise colors has to do with Rayleigh scattering. I spoke with meteorologist Chris Bouchard of the Fairbanks Museum and Planetarium in St. Johnsbury, Vermont, who kindly dropped some knowledge on this scattering business.

Bouchard started off by explaining that the light we receive here on Earth from the sun is white – meaning it is composed of an even mix of all visible colors. But this white light is transformed as it passes through our atmosphere and encounters nitrogen and oxygen molecules, which cause the light beams to "scatter," or change direction. It is this scattering that "paints the sky with color," Bouchard explained. "Because of some fairly complex physics, these gases cause light beams of shorter wavelengths to scatter more than those of longer wavelengths."

Light beams of shorter wavelengths include violet, blue, and green; those with longer wavelengths include red, orange, and yellow. "Violet has the shortest wavelength in the visible spectrum, and so it scatters the most," Bouchard said.

Which begs the question, why isn't our sky violet then, instead of blue?

"Well, in fact it is!" said Bouchard. "It's just that the human eye is more sensitive to blue light than purple, so the sky appears blue."

NOV

At high noon, when the sun is directly overhead, the direct sunlight travels through a relatively small amount of air to reach your eye. During sunrise and sunset, the sun's direct light comes in at an angle, which means that it has to travel through much more air than at noon, explained Bouchard. "Therefore, more cool colors are scattered away from the light beam, causing the tint of what's left of the beam to shift strongly toward the warm end of the scale, causing oranges and reds."

What accounts for sunsets being more stunning in autumn and winter, as opposed to spring and summer? Pollution. Though, if you grew up thinking (as I did) that more car exhaust and smokestack spewage meant better sunset colors, you've got it backwards – for the most part.

"The truth is that tropospheric aerosols [that's pollution] ... do not enhance sky colors, they subdue them. Clean air is, in fact, the main ingredient common to brightly colored sunrises and sunsets," states NOAA's website.

The particulates of atmospheric pollution (like dust, smoke, and vehicle exhaust) are much larger than molecules of gas (like oxygen and nitrogen), making them poor Rayleigh scatterers of color. "In other words, they scatter all colors fairly evenly, much like a fog does," said Bouchard. "Since most air pollution sources are at ground level, particulates tend to collect in the lower atmosphere. Bright sunset colors passing through these hazes tend to be muted and dulled as a result." However, while pollution has a dulling effect on the intensity of colored light, the smog itself can become saturated with that colored light, expanding the coloration of the sunset.

During our summers, particulate concentrations peak because a) winds are lightest, and b) the sun is strongest, which contributes to faster photochemical smog production. Photochemical smog develops when primary pollutants (oxides of nitrogen and volatile organic compounds created from fossil fuel combustion) interact with each other under the influence of sunlight, producing a mixture of different and hazardous chemicals known as secondary pollutants.

"In the colder months, winds stir with more fervor, leading to less concentrated pollutants," Bouchard explained. "Photochemical pollutants are also at a minimum because of the low sun angle and shorter days."

So while you may not welcome the bitter cold of late autumn and winter, you can take some comfort in the seasons' stop-dead-in-your-tracks-and-stare sunsets.

# Buck Meets Doe

JOHN BUCK

One of the evolutionary adjustments whitetail deer have made is to reproduce early and often. A six-year-old whitetail doe can easily become a great-great-grandmother, and she can continue to produce fawns each year until she is ten years old.

Most deer in New Hampshire and Vermont are born in early summer, and they reach sexual maturity when they are little more than a year old. Young bucks start growing their first set of antlers in the summer; young does will be entering their first estrus in November. Female deer can be even more precocious, reaching sexual maturity at six months of age if they live in good habitat. Sexual maturation of both sexes is largely dependent on body size, which in turn depends on habitat quality and age.

Because we live in an area with severe winters, a short, precisely timed breeding season is key to fawn survival. A doe's gestation period is 200 days – if she gives birth too early, a fawn will be exposed to freezing temperatures and the doe may not have sufficient greenery with which to stimulate her milk; if she gives birth too late, the fawn may not be robust enough to survive its first winter.

To address this, deer have a built-in breeding alarm clock that's set by the amount of light in a day. In autumn, the pituitary gland is stimulated into reproductive function by the gradual shortening of the length of time it is exposed to light relayed by the optic nerves. The pituitary regulates the hormones responsible for bucks' sperm production and does' ovulation. The three important hormones are follicle stimulating hormone (FSH), luteinizing hormones (LH), and prolactin or lactogenic hormone (LTH). In bucks, these hormones act together to initiate the production of testosterone, which, along with FSH, enables the manufacture of sperm cells. Testosterone also influences antler development, body strength, and aggressive behavior.

In does, these hormones promote follicle development in the ovaries and the production of estrogen. Estrogen is responsible for increased development of the female sex organs and for the behavioral changes that permit a single buck to court her. Estrogen also prepares the uterus to receive the mature eggs that will soon rupture from the ovaries.

All of this hormonal action comes to fruition around the end of October, when the first does will come into heat. The peak of conception typically occurs the third week of November, followed by very diminished breeding activity into early December. Each doe will be receptive to a buck's courting for just 24 hours. Over the course of the following three weeks, almost every doe in the twin states will go into estrus and, amazingly enough, considering the brief window of opportunity, the great majority of them (over 90 percent) will be bred. Does will give birth the following spring, usually to twins.

Occasionally, conception will not occur, usually because the doe was young or the buck did not have viable sperm. When this happens, the doe will go through her pre-estrus cycle again and become fecund in approximately 28 days. If conception doesn't occur until late December, fawns will not be born until mid-July. This late birthing limits the amount of time for the newborns to grow before the onset of winter and puts them at a distinct disadvantage for survival.

It has happened that a doe will not get bred until a third heat cycle, which means that fawns will be born in August. A fawn born in June can reach 100 pounds by winter; one born in August will have a hard time reaching 50. Still sporting their spots in October as they try to develop their winter coats, the deck is stacked heavily against these late fawns.

The November rifle season for deer in Vermont and New Hampshire is timed to coincide with the primary estrus period for two reasons. First, the young of the year have grown enough to be able to take care of themselves without their mothers' care. Second, it takes advantage of the buck's preoccupation with reproduction. Deer are very wary and difficult to hunt. If it weren't for momentary lapses in defense, hunter success would be a small fraction of the roughly 10 percent in a typical year. This would render hunting useless as a deer herd management tool. The resulting over-population of deer and its devastating effect on the regeneration of the forest would prove to be a huge problem.

# Keep Forests Beautiful: Litter

Joe Rankin

It's one of the pleasures of fall: walking in the woods on a warm day, scuffing my feet through a deep layer of newly fallen leaves. Looking down, I notice the gold coins of aspen leaves against the bread-knife serrations of brown beech leaves. My feet make that "swoosh, swoosh" sound that takes me back to when I was a kid.

It's November, and where I live the color blast has faded. The woods are gray and brown. The much admired "fall foliage" has drifted earthward to become the more prosaic "leaf litter." I understand the term, but the word litter grates a little. It connotes trash, yet leaves are just the opposite of trash. Their contribution to forest health, to the ecosystem, is incalculable. They help make the forest what it is.

Fallen leaves provide insulation from cold, benefiting myriad creatures. They act as mulch, preventing soil drying. They absorb raindrops, which helps prevent erosion during hard rains. And they eventually become soil themselves – that light, airy, fragrant, moist humus that is key to a healthy forest.

Almost the minute a fallen leaf hits the ground, it starts down the path of decay and decomposition. But it's a slow process. Leaves are composed of cellulose and lignin and are a chewy meal.

"They are pretty tough, like everything else in nature. But there are whole groups of organisms that are able to break them down," Kevin Smith told me. Smith is a researcher with the U.S. Forest Service's Northern Research Station in Durham, New Hampshire, and an expert on decay and decomposition in the forest. When he takes a walk in the woods, "a lot of it is on my hands and knees," he said.

Larger animals work to crack leaves into more manageable pieces; every time a wild turkey or ruffed grouse scratches through the leaves, it's doing just that. Millipedes and the tiny terrestrial crustaceans known as pillbugs and sowbugs munch on them. Bacteria and fungi – particularly the ascomycetes, or cup fungi – work diligently to extract what little nutrients there are, the tree having retrieved most of the good stuff – potassium, phosphorus, and nitrogen – before letting the leaves go.

There are a lot of things that determine how fast leaves decay: how much moisture is present, the shape of the leaf, whether it is hairy (hairy is harder for munchers to get a grip on), how much nitrogen is left in it (fungi and bacteria crave nitrogen), if there are tannins (oak leaves have a lot of tannins and are harder to break down), and the proportion of lignin to cellulose (lignins have a chemical structure that's more of a challenge for the decomposers). Some parts of the leaf, especially the stalk or petiole, are much tougher than others.

A recent study by Massachusetts Institute of Technology researchers found that temperature also plays an important role. Though there are innumerable leaf types and lots of variables when it comes to leaf decay, as temperatures rise the rate of decay goes up the same across the board. Their findings, which they've translated into a mathematical model, could help improve climate change models and better predict carbon dioxide levels, because as leaves decay, much of the carbon they free up ends up in the atmosphere as the greenhouse gas carbon dioxide.

In the end, months, perhaps years from now, what will be left of the newest layer of dead leaves in the forest?

Well, not much, Smith said. But what is left is important. It's known as humus.

"Certainly for our northeastern forests, the life of the forest depends on humus. I couldn't say it more strongly," Smith explained.

Humus holds moisture and helps with soil aeration, buffering trees from two of their major stressors: getting their roots waterlogged and having them dry out. It also stores calcium and magnesium, two elements essential for forest health.

Fall, then, is "the time of year when there's this great loading of leaves and organic matter onto the forest floor that will fuel these processes. What we see as the shedding process is a big part of what helps maintain soil fertility and the growth of trees and the next generation of trees," Smith said.

That's why it always pains me when I see people bagging leaves to throw away. I've been known to stop and offer to take them off their hands. I know of a better home for them.

For a fun autumn activity related to this essay, turn to page 210.

# The Apple Bears

Elise Tillinghast

Last week, a black bear in a blaze orange collar showed up in our yard. Two cubs followed close behind. The sow paused to observe the house, then led her cubs up across our field and down into a small stand of apple trees beside the road. There, the family feasted on piles of old apples lying in the grass. They appeared to take a methodical approach, working their way from one tree to the next.

Inside our house, the scene was not nearly as calm. There were rushed attempts at photography, foiled by warped window glass. There was my two-year-old son, precariously balanced on the back of a chair by the window, shrieking "BEAR" and, occasionally, "SHOES" – his way of demanding to go outside.

We did not go outside. We didn't take any good photos, either. Eventually a car on the road scared the bears, and they ran up the hill and back into the woods.

Thanks to that orange collar, I knew that the sow was one of Ben Kilham's research animals. Kilham, a well-known authority on black bears who lives in Lyme, New Hampshire, uses satellite tracking to monitor the movements of several bears in our region. From this data, he has a pretty good sense of how bear travel patterns vary, year to year.

According to Kilham, the sow in our orchard is a four-year-old named "Clarkie." She was born in Dorchester, New Hampshire, and after being chased out of the natal territory by her mother, settled down near Thetford, Vermont.

Typical of female bears, Clarkie has a home range of just a few square miles. Hers happens to be rich in red oaks – which means that her local food supply is subject to the booms and busts of acorn production. In 2014, the oaks produced a heavy crop, so Clarkie had no reason to travel. By late November, she had bred, fattened up, and gone to den. Pregnant females typically begin hibernation before other bears, Kilham explained, provided that they have succeeded in putting on enough weight.

Autumn of 2015 presented more difficult conditions for Clarkie. The acorn crop was meager, and there was intense competition from other nut eaters – a proliferation of rodents that resulted from the previous good mast year. Chipmunks, especially, are "major competitors to black bears," said Kilham. He noted that beech nut production was also "spotty" this year. Although some sows in heavy beech stands were able to stay home, for Clarkie and many other bears, local beech trees didn't produce enough mast to meet their nutritional needs.

On top of the acorn scarcity is a second challenge for Clarkie: her status as a first-time mother of twins. The sow is working to put on hibernation weight while also still nursing her young, each the approximate size of a Labrador retriever.

All this sounded pretty dire to me, but Kilham seemed to think that the region's bears in general, and Clarkie in particular, were having a decent year. He described the fall's superabundant apple crop as a major boon.

While it's hard to imagine getting fat on apples, Kilham said that bears succeed by digesting a lot of them quickly, instead of eking out every calorie from each piece of fruit. This wham bam approach is why the keen observer may find loose-looking bear poop right now, adorned with bright red apple chunks.

Since returning from a foray across the river to Smart's Mountain, where they fed on beech nuts, Clarkie and her cubs have been on the hunt for apples. "It's all the bears are eating now," said Kilham.

In addition to making the rounds among apple trees in Thetford, they have passed through Fairlee, and crossed the interstate up in Bradford. There, the bears lingered for approximately 10 hours beside the road. (Kilham explained they were probably waiting to cross until traffic calmed, a behavior he has observed in another one of his research bears.) For the most part, said Kilham, they are near houses only at night, and go unnoticed by humans.

Contemplating Clarkie's travels, my takeaway is that the value of wildlife corridors – linkage areas that allow wild animals to move from one block of habitat to another – can't be adequately assessed in any one year. Access routes that are irrelevant to Clarkie and her kin in one year may be critical to their survival in the next.

When one talks about the benefits of connected habitat, conversations can get wonky, fast. But for me, on a cold afternoon in November, what it came down to was this: three glossy black bears with apple breath, and my human cub at the window, shrieking in delight.

# Owl Pellets: Down the Hatch and Back Again

LEAH BURDICK

"She's so cute!" a little girl coos to the snowy white owl. The owl blinks languidly, ignoring her admirer. No doubt she is used to human attention, as she is one of the more popular raptors housed at the Vermont Institute of Natural Science Nature Center (VINS) in Quechee, Vermont. She likewise ignores the decapitated rat in her food bowl, chirruping softly as if dissatisfied with what's on the menu. I wait patiently, hoping to witness the moment when she gulps it down.

Owls eat their smaller prey whole, or tear larger prey into chunks with their beaks and talons. Sooner or later, that owl will grab the raw rat out of her food bowl with her sharp beak and knock it back like a shot of whisky. It will slide down her esophagus and into her two-chambered stomach. The first chamber, called the proventriculus, or glandular stomach, secretes digestive enzymes to break down all the easily digestible parts. Much like our own stomach, this chamber will liquefy the soft tissue (the gooey stuff, including muscle, fat, and organs). Whatever isn't digested in the first chamber, such as the bones, fur and teeth, will pass through to the second chamber, called the gizzard.

All birds have gizzards, although not all birds regurgitate pellets. Some gizzards are larger and stronger than others, adapted to what kinds of food a species eats. The gizzard is made of thick muscles that grind down the tougher parts of a bird's meal, moving all the soft material through to the intestines. Some birds with very muscular gizzards even eat small stones and grit to help grind down bones. In birds that regurgitate, the hard, indigestible material is compressed by the gizzard into a pellet.

Unlike most birds, owls do not have a baglike organ called a *crop* in their throat, which stores food to be digested later. Whenever the owl eats, she will start to digest immediately. Good thing, too, for the owl can't eat again until that pellet has been ejected; it takes up too much room in the stomach. Although horking up a packet of bones after every meal might seem uncomfortable, the process is actually thought to be vital for the owl's health. As the pellet travels up the digestive tract, it scours her throat clean.

Owls often return to the same perches for regurgitation, and you'll often find piles of pellets lying around the base of a favored tree. At first glance, disgorged pellets look more like scat than regurgitations, as the pellet is squished into the oblong shape of the gizzard. Upon closer inspection, a plethora of tiny white bones can be found, nestled in hair and fur. With patience and a steady hand, the prey's entire skeleton can be reassembled.

Dissecting owl pellets is an excellent introduction to the complexity of the food chain and predator/prey relationships. Not only do owl pellets contain the bones of their prey, they are also ecosystems unto themselves, containing fungi, beetles, moth larvae, and caterpillar droppings. The pellets carry potentially harmful viruses and bacteria, so if you'd like to dissect a found pellet, you might want to handle it with gloves and put it in the microwave for a minute or so, to sterilize it. Or, a short cut: the Montshire Museum of Science in Norwich, Vermont, sells a popular sterilized pellet dissection kit in its gift shop. For bulk orders, VINS collects all the bird pellets from the animal enclosures every day, separates the pellets by species, and freezes them to sell for a nominal fee, mostly to schools and nature camps.

Back at the enclosure, I wait and watch the owl as she sits on her post, still ignoring the rat. Born and bred in captivity, she evidently has none of the urgency of a wild bird to secure its next meal. Slowly, her beautiful white head turns, and piercing yellow eyes blink.

*I see you.*

I stare back. She tilts her head and trills low in her throat. Then her head casually swivels away, dismissing me, and at least for now, her dinner, as she fluffs her mottled feathers to settle back on her perch.

# december

# December

## first week

Acorn weevil larvae will spend the winter in the soil after chewing their way out of an acorn.

Painted turtles often delay hibernation and can be seen swimming below pond ice.

The red caps of British soldier lichen are fungal fruiting bodies. They have to hook up with the correct alga before life can proceed.

Now that adult insects are scarce, downy woodpeckers seek the larvae of the goldenrod gall fly, which overwinter inside goldenrod balls.

## second week

Dec 13-14: Peak of the Geminids, one of the best meteor showers of the year, but sometimes the moon interferes.

During very cold weather barred owls may do some daytime hunting.

The blue berries of blue cohosh may still be hanging onto the plant's smooth, tan stalks.

Many seed-eating larvae live inside the seed heads of staghorn sumac. The chickadees pecking at sumac fruit may be seeking out caterpillars in addition to seeds.

# third week

Dec 21 or 22: Winter solstice: the longest night of the year in the northern hemisphere.

The winter diet of the snowshoe hare features the twigs and buds of sugar maple, aspen, white pine, hemlock, and beaked hazelnut.

Brains are expensive to maintain, so the part of a chickadee's brain that deals with song shrinks considerably in the winter.

The berries of wild roses that persist into winter are high on the list of winter food for mammals and birds.

# fourth week

Hawthorn fruits are nobody's favorite, but they stay on the tree and are valuable emergency food.

Golden-crowned kinglets are the smallest of our winter birds. They are often tame and can be seen feeding on insects and spiders, usually in softwoods.

After the first deep snow, deer will head for deeryards, usually south- or west-facing slopes with dense softwood cover.

You can confidently blame the porcupine for any extensive barking high in a tree.

# Does This Fur Make Me Look Fat?

LI SHEN

Fat gets a bad rap in the medical world, for good reason. Excessive body fat is linked to a litany of health risks, including diabetes, heart disease, high blood pressure, and stroke. Yet in the realm of nature, fat is a lifesaver. If certain mammals that hibernate did not get fat, they would be dead by spring.

The woodchuck is something of a fat specialist. As many an irate gardener can attest, the woodchuck's diet consists of perishable greens. Because these can't be stored, the animal stockpiles all the food energy it needs to survive winter in a thick layer of body fat.

Between spring, when a woodchuck first emerges, and late fall, when hibernation begins, the woodchuck doubles its body weight. Every day that it can eat without interruption improves its survival prospects. (For this reason, live trapping and relocation of woodchucks may doom them, as they will have to spend a lot of time and energy getting established in a new territory. The stress of moving and disruption of feeding can easily result in more loss of fat than animals can replace.)

As winter approaches, the woodchuck excavates a burrow that reaches deep underground below the frost line. Unlike the rambling summer burrow that has at least two entrances (main entrance and emergency exit), the winter burrow has only one. The woodchuck enters hibernation sometime in October, curling up on a bed of grass and sealing the entrance to its winter burrow with dirt.

Full hibernation is more than mere sleep. Body processes grind virtually to a standstill. Heart rate slows from 80-95 to about 3 beats a minute. Breathing slows to one breath every few minutes and body temperature drops to a few degrees above burrow temperature, about 40 degrees. It is remarkable – and baffling to scientists – that these changes do not result in death, since a normal mammal heart stops beating at 50 to 70 degrees (body temperature).

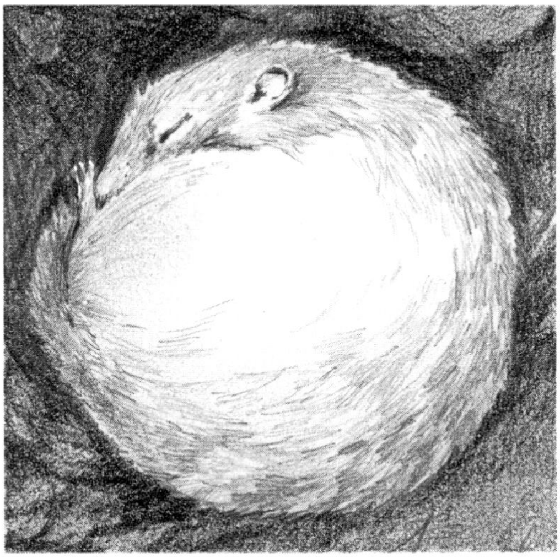

Only 10 percent of the fat stores are burned while the woodchuck is in a deep hibernation state. However, there is periodic awakening every 10 days or so. The animal's body heats up, heartbeat and breathing return to normal levels, and the animal becomes alert. There are various theories as to why arousal is necessary. One is that hibernation is not true sleep, and the brain requires periods of sleep in order to maintain itself. So, paradoxically, woodchucks may wake up to sleep.

Another theory is that this return to normal metabolism is needed for immune system function. Woodchucks often harbor bacteria associated with pneumonia, and suffer from high incidences of this disease by the end of winter, most likely from the stale air in the burrow. Whatever the reason, awakening during hibernation must be essential, as it represents a significant energy investment. Approximately 90 percent of the fat stores are burned during these periods.

What causes hibernation? Apparently not seasonal clues, since captive woodchucks kept indoors and given supplemental light still get fat and go into hibernation. Interestingly, a crude extract from the blood of hibernating woodchucks caused nonhibernating woodchucks to begin hibernating. The mystery blood compound has provoked mind-boggling visions of human hibernation during intergalactic space travel. However, so far, all attempts to isolate the compound have been unsuccessful.

Despite their diligent preparation, many woodchucks die in hibernation. While running out of fat does not seem to be the direct cause of death, it is known that fatter woodchucks survive better. First-year woodchucks have higher mortality rates than older woodchucks, and the youngsters with the highest mortality are the ones born latest in the year. Being underweight is thought to make them more susceptible to winter diseases.

Awareness of the woodchuck's winter survival challenges may help us forgive their rampages through the summer garden. What looks like gluttony to humans is in fact merely sensible eating behavior for animals who fast all winter. While many of us may soon be regretting a holiday food binge, chances are that no woodchuck has ever worried about being too fat.

# A Christmas Tree Farmer's Year in Review

PATRICK WHITE

Walking through a large chain store this past October – at least a week before Halloween – I stumbled upon a display of decorations. Not witches and pumpkins, but trees and bells. There's no question that retailers are intent on pushing the start of the Christmas season earlier and earlier, but we Christmas tree growers still have them beat; for us, it's a nearly year-round endeavor.

Spring is one of the busiest times on a Christmas tree farm, yet it sometimes requires an agonizingly long wait before work can get started. It can take weeks of warmer weather to thaw the soil enough to plant the next rotation of trees.

Large tree farms often use planting machines pulled by tractors. Hand-planting – using either a special spade or motorized auger – is much slower, but it's the method that we and many other farms rely on because we are interplanting among larger trees (in spaces where trees were cut the prior season) that prevent a tractor from passing through.

In late spring, the hillsides seem to come back to life with the growth of new leaves on deciduous trees. Harder to spot in the distance is the new growth of evergreens. But most Christmas tree growers are out in their fields at this time of year, carefully monitoring their trees as the buds on the end of each branch redden and swell and finally "break" to allow new tender shoots to emerge. The process is a marvel to observe, and sometimes it's possible to see progress hour to hour on a warm spring day. Trees are particularly vulnerable at this time of year; once bud-break occurs, a late frost can kill off any new growth, effectively stunting the tree for a year.

DEC

In late June, it's time to begin the process of shearing (shaping) each tree. It's a tough chore, usually done manually by swinging a long, sharp knife at an angle to create the traditional conical Christmas tree shape. Hand pruners are used to eliminate double (or triple) leaders at the tops of the trees. Birds love to land on these tall tops, which causes many to break off while still tender. That's why many growers wait until the new growth has completely hardened before selecting the best top and cutting out the others.

Another summer job is mowing between the rows of trees; the goal is to keep grass and weeds from overtaking the trees, as well as to help promote air circulation that can reduce the risks of some needle diseases, and to make it easier to walk and work in the field. I hold off as long as possible on my first mowing each year in order to allow bobolinks and other grassland birds time to nest. There are others using the tall grass, too: One year I was mowing when something ahead caught my eye and caused me to slam on the brakes: a young fawn was lying almost completely hidden from view.

It was yet another reminder that we're not alone in calling this farm our home. Nearly every time I walk through the trees I have some sort of wildlife interaction: deer grazing, turkeys marching, songbirds nesting, butterflies, foxes, rabbits, moles, even the occasional turtle.

Fall usually means finishing up the shearing that was begun in early summer. It's the most pleasant time of the year to work, with none of summer's salty sweat running into my eyes. In the fall I find I'm more apt to take breaks and just sit to look: at the trees I've been shaping for months, at the colors beginning to change on hillsides in the distance, at the crickets and grasshoppers that seem to cover every inch of the field.

Late fall brings a whole new look to the farm. I'm not sure why, but once the first hard frost hits, the trees seem to turn at least one shade darker green. That's when I know it's time to turn some attention to the logistics of selling trees (ordering hot chocolate, placing advertisements, setting up the parking area, decorating wreaths). Every year, we are fortunate to be visited by hundreds of eager families, all searching for their perfect tree. Little do most of them realize all the activity that takes place here the rest of the year, long before Bing Crosby and Burl Ives take over the radio airwaves.

# Winter's Little King

KENRICK VEZINA

The only regal thing about the golden-crowned kinglet is the crest of yellow-orange feathers atop its head. Everything else about this speck of a songbird's appearance and behavior would make any proper monarch frown. It's half the size of a black-capped chickadee yet twice as energetic: a gregarious and kinetic bird wrapped in unassuming olive-gray plumage. Yet this tiny creature faces head-on winters that animals 15,000 times its size (we're looking at you, black bears) hide from.

Winter survival for animals in the Northeast often involves setting their metabolisms to "simmer" and waiting out the coldest months in a state of hibernation (in the case of many mammals) or some equivalent torpor (most reptiles, insects, amphibians). In the most dramatic cases (wood frogs, woolly-bear caterpillars), the animals simply freeze solid and thaw in spring. Songbirds, given the luxury of flight, often simply flee.

The golden-crowned kinglet – despite weighing barely more than a quarter, with a length of three to four inches, half of that being tail – uses none of the above tricks. When most of our forests hunker down, enter stasis, the kinglet kicks its frenetic lifestyle into high gear.

It has to.

Unlike larger year-round songbirds that huddle up, puff their feathers, tuck in their heads, and become spheres of conserved energy, the tiny golden-crowned kinglet takes no such breaks. Its metabolism runs hot, even for a bird. Accordingly, the kinglet responds to winter's cold by going hyperactive.

You'd be forgiven for expecting kinglets to have a varied diet of seeds and other foodstuffs that are – with a bit of effort – available in winter. This is, after all, how small birds like chickadees and titmice get by. The catch is that golden-crowned kinglets are almost exclusively insectivores. Oh, they might eat tiny bits of plant matter in winter, but the vast majority of their diet remains soft-bodied arthropods like mites, caterpillars, and spiders.

So if you notice that winter flocks of kinglets seem a bit manic, it's because they spend literally the entire day foraging. They're not flitting about for the sheer joy of it; every brief hover near the tip of a branch is a scan for the sparse insect food that is available in winter, an act of purest necessity. Eventually, no matter how early they rise, daylight ends. Temperatures drop. Even this brassy bird needs to put on the brakes for a winter's night. And this is where things get mysterious.

Ornithologists agree that the kinglet simply doesn't have enough capacity for energy storage to make it through the night unaided, no matter how many mites it devours. And particularly cold nights can be a death sentence that wipes out entire micropopulations. But, on balance, they do survive. Not only are they common across North America, their populations are of least concern to conservationists.

Theories on how these birds make it through the winter night conflict. Some argue that they must lower their metabolism and go into controlled hypothermia to survive, but no one has ever documented them doing so. Some populations seek shelter in abandoned squirrel nests, but despite an intensive study in Maine, naturalist Bernd Heinrich couldn't find any evidence of his kinglets doing the same. Some huddle together in small groups in the dense branches of conifers, so many Lilliputian furnaces keeping each other warm. On the whole, though, the night is a dark spot in our knowledge of golden-crowed kinglets.

What we do know about the golden-crowned kinglet's winter lifestyle is nothing short of astonishing. Here's a bird that breaks all the rules of winter survival, and despite heavy attrition, continues to prosper.

It may have gotten its regal name from a quick glance at its sun-bright crest, but make no mistake: winter's little king has earned its crown.

# Under the Water, December's Peak Leaf Season

Declan McCabe

By December, foliage season is long over for us humans, but it's peak season under the water. Last month, as the last bus of tourists departed for home, fallen leaves accumulated in our streams and rivers, starting a process that's critical for the nourishment of everything from caddisflies on up the food chain to eagles and even humans. In fact, most of a New England stream's food supply originates in the form of fallen leaves.

The bright yellow and red piles that accumulate on river rocks and fallen branches are not nearly ready for consumption by discerning invertebrates. The witch's brew of natural chemical compounds that discourages insects from eating green leaves on trees can be just as repellent to creatures that scavenge freshly fallen leaves underwater. First, cold water must leach out those chemicals. Imagine the process as soaking and resoaking a teabag. During this period, the leaves are also colonized by microscopic organisms. For a hungry invertebrate, the cleansed layered leaves, covered in fungi, bacteria, and algae, make a sandwich of which Dagwood Bumstead could be proud.

If all leaves were created equal, then the river food supply would consist of a brief crop polished off by whatever ravenous insect species got there first. But of course not all tree and shrub species lose their foliage at exactly the same time, and their leaves decompose at different rates. Some are tough, leathery, and laden with toxins. Certain laurel species can release so much cyanide that entomologists have used them to kill study specimens. Other species, such as linden, are comparatively soft and become an early underwater food source. Oaks and beech trees hold onto their tough leaves late into the season and when they finally fall, they are slow to reach an edible condition.

Variability in the timing of leaf fall, and in the rates at which leaves become palatable, means that edible leaves are available for most of the winter. This is also the season when much aquatic invertebrate growth occurs. A caddisfly species called *Pycnopsyche gentilis* acts like a chronicler of the leaf supply. In fall and early winter, its larvae cut disks from leaves, and use silk to make and line pencil-diameter cases in which they live. In early spring, as leaves become scarce and the larvae keep growing, they add to their cases using large sand grains. This is why one can sometimes find cases with leaves at the back end and sand grains at the front.

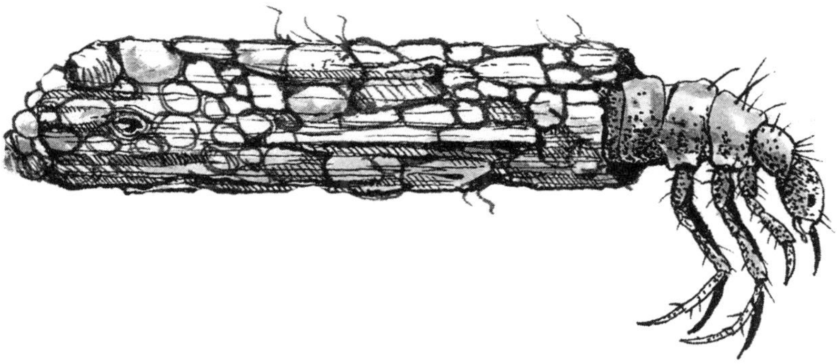

Although fish aren't typically leaf-eaters, they nonetheless rely on the underwater foliage season. Cranefly larvae and stoneflies, fattened up on leaves, are protein-packed snacks for hungry trout, salmon, and bass. Without invertebrates, fish would go hungry. Without some knowledge of invertebrates, few anglers would know what to put on a hook to lure a spectacular brook trout.

Cleanest streams host most invertebrate species and simply counting the number of species can be the basis for an interesting study. For example, each fall, I visit forested and urban streams with Saint Michael's College biology students. One year we found more than 20 species in Browns River, downstream from Mount Mansfield State Forest. Centennial Brook drains South Burlington neighborhoods and parking lots, and hosts fewer than half that many invertebrate species. Browns River macroinvertebrates include clean-water-loving giant stoneflies, and an assortment of mayflies. I have yet to meet a Centennial Brook stonefly, because the community is dominated by midges, craneflies, and a particularly tough caddisfly that makes its living by filtering particles from the water.

A view into the world of submerged invertebrates is just a bunch of leaves away. You can easily lift an intact chunk of leafy habitat from a streambed for study. Equipment can be as simple as a basin of stream water. Drop a handful of streambed leaves into the basin and observations can begin. Rinse and remove the leaves one at a time to reveal the small creatures living among them.

# Pine on the Cob

Michael J. Caduto

A few summers ago, I saw a red squirrel skittering along the top of a stone wall with something in its mouth. I snuck in closer and discovered the headless body of a chipmunk dangling from its jaws. Prior to that, I'd viewed red squirrels as curmudgeonly little herbivores, not wolves in squirrel's clothing. It was as if Bugs Bunny had eaten the head off of Alvin the Chipmunk.

The cantankerous red squirrels are opportunistic feeders. Their diet consists mostly of vegetarian fare, but in addition to eating nuts, bark, roots, fruit, fungi, buds, and flowers, they'll partake of everything from insects, eggs, and baby birds to small reptiles, amphibians, mice, baby rabbits, and even cast-off antlers.

During the winter, red squirrels subsist on seeds of cones and may eat up to two-thirds of the pine seed crop produced in a forest each year. Other staples include the seeds of spruce and eastern hemlock, but they'll also eat those of cedar, larch, and many hardwoods. One study of captive red squirrels found that each squirrel consumed the seeds from an average of 144 white spruce cones each day. Because Norway spruce cones contain numerous high-energy seeds that store especially well, groves of this tree can harbor four to five times the number of red squirrels found in other conifer forests.

I've observed red squirrels biting off white pine cones, which land with a "thump" about every 10 seconds. When watching a squirrel forage amid Norway spruce, I saw it carry away cones almost as long as its seven-inch body. Most cones are cached in the shade of mature conifers – hoarded for the winter either individually or in mounds called middens that are secreted underground, beneath rocks, or in hollow trees. A red squirrel's acute sense of smell can detect seed caches buried under a foot of soil and beneath snow up to 12 feet deep.

DEC

One fascinating study of red squirrel behavior conducted by Fritz Gerhardt in a grove of Norway spruce in Norwich, Vermont, found that the squirrels habitually raid each other's middens. On average, each squirrel saw about a quarter of its seeds stolen by neighbors, while simultaneously stealing about the same proportion of seeds from surrounding middens. However, some squirrels pilfered far more seeds than they had stolen from them, and vice versa, so the actual balance varied between neighboring squirrels.

A red squirrel will frequent the base of a particular pine tree to eat, chewing scales off the core of a cone the way people eat corn-on-the-cob. First, it chews the scales off near the stem. As each scale falls away, a pair of seeds is exposed. Because each subsequent scale lies up the cone and a small turn along the spiral, the squirrel must twirl the cone as it eats. Mounds of discarded scales and naked cone-cores pile up wherever a red squirrel partakes of its pine-on-the-cob.

Terminal conifer buds are another winter staple. Like cones, red squirrels harvest buds using the gnaw-and-drop method. They also munch the buds of maples and birches. In some spruce forests, I've seen the ground littered with thousands of branch tips. Although red squirrels look comically mischievous with their black eyes surrounded by white rings, their heavy harvest of seeds and buds, and their penchant for eating the bark of young trees, can seriously damage conifers and their ability to regenerate.

But red squirrels don't just gnaw the winter away. When not active by day, they hunker down in tree hollows, rocky enclaves, and underground burrows. During extreme cold, these solitary creatures sometimes share shelters. Otherwise they defend territories with vociferous screeches, buzzes, and grating, rhythmic chortlings. In good coniferous forest, red squirrel territories range up to two acres.

They breed from about mid-January through mid-February, often during thaws. Dens are in hollow trees, especially old woodpecker nests. Litters of two to five hairless squirrellets arrive about a month after mating. Young grow quickly under the female's care, start to wander from the nest at around six weeks, and are weaned in about two months. Goshawks, martens, red-tailed hawks, ermines, red foxes, and other predators eat so many young that only a quarter survive to reproduce the following year.

As winter progresses and sap starts to flow, red squirrels sometimes chew holes in the bark of sugar maples and other hardwoods. After the sap oozes out and evaporation concentrates the sugar, the squirrels return to lap up the sweetness. Europeans who first came to New England learned maple sugaring from indigenous peoples, but we'll never know how red squirrels figured it out. That closely guarded secret is only handed down on a need-to-gnaw basis.

For a fun winter activity related to this essay, turn to page 216.

# Subnivean Zone: Shelter in the Snow

BARBARA MACKAY

Every animal must develop its own way of dealing with winter. Migrate, hibernate, or insulate; these are common strategies. For a few small mammals, survival depends on the snow itself, and the deeper the better.

The subnivean zone is the area between the surface of the ground and the bottom of the snowpack. The word subnivean comes from the Latin "sub" (under) and "nives" (snow). Mice, voles, and shrews retreat here for protection from cold temperatures, bitter winds, and hungry predators. Food is right at hand: grass, leaves, bark, seeds, and insects are free and unfrozen. Under the snow, these tiny mammals create long tunnel systems complete with air shafts to the surface above.

The subnivean zone begins to form with the first snowfall that lingers. Two things happen. First, some of the snow lands directly on hardy vegetation and overhanging rocks, blocking snow from accumulating underneath. If the plants have already frozen by this time, they are able to hold up subsequent snows like little umbrellas. Eventually, the weight causes the slender tips to droop to the ground, creating a protected area perfect for hideaways and runways.

At the same time, the snow that lands on the ground sublimates; that is, changes from a solid into a gas without going through the melting stage. Sublimation is prompted by heat radiating from the earth. Warm, moist water vapor rising into the bottom layer of snow cools, condenses, and refreezes into tightly packed, rounded ice crystals.

It takes only six inches of snow for mice, voles, and shrews to have a sturdy roof over their heads and roomy living quarters below. Add another two inches and the subnivean zone remains within a degree or two of 32, regardless of the temperature and weather conditions in the outside world.

It is easy enough to study this hidden habitat. Look for an air hole in the snow and dig a pit straight down next to it. If you're lucky, you may discover an intricate system of rooms and hallways. The most elaborate contain a sleeping area, a breakfast nook, a food cache corner, and a latrine. Long, narrow tunnels connect everything. For convenience, most tunnels begin where there is a tree trunk, large rock, or thick bush. These dark surfaces also absorb solar heat, helping to moderate the temperature of the animals, the plants, and the ground itself.

Living under the snow is not without risk. Owls can hear mice and voles running around underground from 30 yards away. With balled-up feet, they crash through the top crust and all the layers of snow to grab their prey. Foxes and coyotes detect by scent. With an acrobatic pounce, these predators will dive right in for their meal. Suffocation is a hazard for those left behind in a collapsed tunnel.

Another predator is the ermine, a white weasel with a black-tipped tail. Its long, slender body can easily squeeze down narrow air shafts. It boldly enters a mouse's domain and fills up on its favorite food. To add insult to injury, it will sometimes build a nest of mouse fur and usurp the tunnel system for its own. It doesn't stay long, but unfortunately no one is left to appreciate that.

Come spring, the subnivean dwellers (and any weasel still pursuing them) face other challenges. A sudden thaw or early rain can drown them as water floods their home. The conditions that stir sugar maples to life also cause the snow to alternately thaw and freeze, weakening its structure. One day the snowpack will collapse, often with a pronounced "whumph." There does not seem to be any depletion of the mice and vole population (at my house, anyway); perhaps the awakening of dormant roots and shoots has alerted the mammals that it's time to vacate the premises.

As spring progresses and all but the last few inches of snow melts, the ingenuity of subnivean survival is spelled out like a map: telltale humps appear where tunnels had crisscrossed the field from tree to rock and beyond. And unlike an abandoned bear den or the deer browse line, all evidence of this survival strategy will disappear when the grass greens up.

# Activities

BARBARA MACKAY

## spring



## summer



## autumn



## winter

# Dandelions: Make Salad, Not War, with Lawn Invaders

Dandelions grow best in sunny spots. Before you pluck them for the following activities, take time to examine their unique composition. *Hands-On Nature*, published by the Vermont Institute for Natural Science, has sketches and descriptions of the parts of the dandelion plant.

You can keep dandelion flower heads fresh for two or three days if you snap them off with your fingers and float them in a shallow bowl of water.

## activity 1

DANDELION STAGES
leaves, bud, flower, seeds

**Materials**:
scissors

**Procedure**:
1. Select two dandelions that can be spared from the lawn mower. Cut them close to the ground. Check the spots each day. How many days does it take for new leaves, buds, and flowers to grow? What time does the flower open and close every day? After the flower reaches peak maturity, let it go to seed. How many days does that take?
2. Blow on one of the fluffy seed heads as hard as you can on a calm day with no breeze. Notice how far the seeds go. Blow the seeds from the other dandelion on a windy day. How far do these seeds go? Compare this distance to the one when there was no breeze.

## activity 2

STRETCHY RUBBER

**Materials**:
collection of fresh dandelions with long stems

**Procedure**:
1. Cover a finger with the sap of seven or eight cut dandelion stems.
2. Let the sticky stuff dry for a few minutes.
3. Roll the dried goo off the top of your finger. Voila! You have a short piece of stretchable rubber.

## activity 3

YELLOW DYE

**Materials**:
4 cups of dandelion flower heads (include goldenrod and/or marigold flowers for a deeper yellow color)

stainless steel pot

4 tablespoons white vinegar

wooden spoon

strainer or colander

glass jar to store dye

**Procedure**:
1. Place the flowers in the pot. Add a quart of water. (Add more water if necessary to just cover the flowers.) Add the vinegar and stir everything together.
2. Bring the water to a boil, then reduce to a simmer.
3. Simmer uncovered for about an hour. Add more water if necessary to keep flowers covered. Stir occasionally.
4. Remove the pot from the heat. Cool the dyed solution while still in the pot. (This may take a couple of hours.)
5. Strain the flower pieces, reserving the dyed water. Store the dye in the refrigerator in a glass container.

*Note: The hot solution in Step 4 can be used immediately. Strain as in Step 5, dye your articles, and dispose of the water when done.*

# activity 4

DANDELIONS FOR DINNER

A number of recipes starring dandelions can be found in foraging books and online. The following suggestions are tasty and easy enough to do with children. A trowel and pair of scissors are good tools to have along when you forage. A collecting basket is helpful, too.

**Leaves**: Dandelion leaves can be eaten raw in an early spring salad, or steamed or sautéed as a cooked green. Younger leaves are less bitter than older, larger leaves.

**Buds**: The tight white buds can be boiled for five to ten minutes and served with butter. Add a dash of vinegar for a pickled taste.

**Yellow flower heads**: These can be frittered by dipping the whole flower head into a thin batter and then frying lightly. Laura Casey of Putney, Vermont, shared this recipe for dandelion marmalade (adapted slightly for this book):

**Ingredients**:

6 oranges and 2 lemons

2 cups dandelion flowers – separate the flower petals from the green parts before measuring (a little green is OK, but too much will make the jelly bitter)

1 box pectin, lower sugar recipe

5 cups sugar

2 1/2 cups water

**Directions**:

1. Peel oranges and one lemon. Chop peel into tiny pieces.
2. Combine with water in a pot. Bring to a boil, then reduce to low heat and simmer for 20 minutes (the mixture should be steaming, not bubbling).
3. Peel and discard the rest of the white rind.
4. Chop oranges and remaining lemon into small chunks. Add to the mixture. Cook 12 minutes.
5. In a bowl, mix pectin and 1 cup sugar.
6. Add the pectin/sugar mixture and dandelion flowers to the mixture in the pot. Cook until boiling. (You can add more water if mixture becomes dry.)
7. Add the 4 remaining cups of sugar. Stirring constantly, return to a full boil. Boil 1 minute, stirring the whole time.
8. Ladle into hot, sterilized jars. The mixture should not be very thick at this point – it may take a week to set. Process in a hot water bath for 10 minutes.

*This recipe can be halved. Note as well that different types of pectin have different properties, so you may need to alter the recipe slightly depending on its properties.*

**Taproot**: Dig deeply to get as much of the root as possible. Wash the dirt off, slice into coins, and boil as you would carrots. The root also makes a robust drink: slice into thin pieces, roast in a 300-degree oven until the pieces are dried but not crisp, mash with a mortar and pestle, and brew as coffee or steep in a tea ball. Small amounts are also good mixed into a vanilla yogurt smoothie.

# activity 5

GROW YOUR OWN DANDELIONS

(from *Hands-On Nature*)

**Materials**:

dandelion taproot
dandelion seeds, moistened
small plant pots
soil
sharp knife

**Procedure**:

1. Cut the taproot into various-sized pieces. Plant these in small pots.
2. At the same time, plant dandelion seeds in other pots.
3. What size root piece will grow a new plant? How long does it take the seeds to grow? Which method makes a new plant faster?

# Sneaky Plants and Gullible Ants

The next time you are in the woods admiring a patch of trilliums or trout lilies, consider how they came to be a patch. One possibility is myrmecochory, seed dispersal by ants. Locate a few wildflowers that let ants do some of the work for them, and come back several more times to watch the seed pods develop.

## activity 1

### ANTS IN THE WOODS

**Materials**:
wildflower field guide
small, sharp knife
magnifying glass

**Preparation**:
Prepare a list of early spring woodland wildflowers that bloom in your area. Some examples might be hepatica, bloodroot, trout lily, spring beauty, trillium, violets, Dutchman's breeches, gaywings, pink corydalis, and wild ginger. All of these plants have seeds with elaiosomes that attract ants.

**Procedure**:

1. As snow retreats from the woods, begin your search for wildflowers in shaded, moist, forested areas. Take note of their locations.

2. Early spring wildflowers are ephemeral, blossoming for a brief period of time, sometimes just a few days. Continue your search as some species' flowers fall off and other varieties come into bloom. The more "sneaky plants" you can find, the better your chances of catching "gullible ants" absconding with the seeds later.

3. After the flower falls off, a seed pod develops. Depending on the species, it can take from a few weeks to a few months for the seeds to mature. Keep checking your patches of identified plants. While you wait, try Activity Two.

4. Ripe fruit looks like it is about to burst. If the pod is very hard and tight, it is probably not ready for field investigation. Check back every few days.

5. When one of the wildflowers has a mature seed pod, examine it closely. Squeeze it gently. How many seeds do you think you will find inside? Carefully open it with your fingernail or knife. What color and shape are the seeds? Are they bigger or smaller than you expected? Some flowers produce only a small number of seeds; can you count the ones in the pod you opened?

6. Examine the yellow-white fatty elaiosomes. Stroke one gently. Is it smooth? Sticky? Oily? Firm? Does it have a scent?

7. Find a seed pod that has already burst open and attracted ants. How do they remove a seed? Does each ant take its own seed, or do they appear to be working together?

8. Watch where the ants take the seeds. Their nest is typically only a few meters away. Do the ants carry the seeds, or do they drag or push them? Do they appear to take rest breaks? How long does it take an ant (or ant pair) to get a seed from the pod to a nest?

9. Place some seeds with elaiosomes on the ground halfway between the plant and the ants' nest. Do ants find and claim these seeds, too?

# activity 2

ANTS AT THE EDGE OF THE WOODS

**Materials**:
five bottle caps or small jar lids (they should all be the same size)

five bait foods, such as cookie crumbles (pecan sandies work well)

oily canned tuna

brown sugar

jelly

crackers

cheese, or a piece of fruit

container to carry the caps/lids to an ant hill or nest

thick stick about six inches long

**Preparation**:
Fill each cap or jar lid with a tablespoon of a different bait.

**Procedure**:
1. Find an active colony of ants at the edge of the woods or in your yard.

2. Place the caps of bait next to each other in a line about a foot away from the ant hill or nest.

3. Observe how long it takes an ant to discover your bait. What does it do next? Usually the ant will go back to the colony to communicate about the food source. It leaves a scent trail so that other ants can find the food, too. Do you see the ants tapping their antennae on the ground to pick up the trail?

4. Ants also use their antennae to taste the food. Observe how they do this.

5. Do they show a preference for one of the baits over the others? Are any of the foods completely rejected after a taste?

6. Remove all of the caps. With your hand, sweep the ground between the nest and where the caps were. Gently sweep aside any ants there, too. Sweeping the ground removes the scent trail.

7. Put the cap with the most popular food back on the ground in the same place it had been. Place the stick a couple of inches in front of it to act as a barrier to the food.

8. What do the ants do when they reach the barrier? How long does it take them to figure out a way to get to the food? Ants lick, touch, and smell each other to communicate. Do you observe these behaviors?

9. Turn the stick 90 degrees. What do the ants do when they reach the stick now? Their scent trail is facing a different direction – do they follow it? How long does it take them to create a new trail to the food? Is it over the stick or around it? Ants are great problem solvers!

# Migrators Spring Forward with New Season

Phenology is the study of seasonal life cycles and events. When you use past observations to predict your first robin sighting, you are engaging in phenology. One rough rule of thumb is derived from Hopkins' Law (also called the "Bioclimatic Law"), which says that many signs of spring move north at a rate of four days for each degree of latitude, or about seventeen miles per day. For every 100 feet of altitude, add another day. This applies until early June. Autumn follows the same pattern moving south, a phenomenon clearly visible on fall foliage.

Don't wait until the snow melts to look for signs of spring. Here are three ways to bridge the gap between sledding and swimming.

## activity 1

### KEEP A PHENOLOGY RECORD

Record phenological observations on a chart or table, such as the sample below. If you use the same format every year, you should be able to see patterns that help predict the progression of spring in your area.

| **Observations** | **Date first seen/heard** | **Temperature/ Location** | **Weather** | **Notes** |
|---|---|---|---|---|
| pussy willows | 3/23 | fishing access | 31° setting sun, cool breeze | |
| robin | 3/25 | front yard | 33° snowed most of the morning | arrived afternoon, some snow melt |
| mourning cloak butterfly | 4/17 | Eden/ Ritterbush | 70° cloudless bright blue sky | |
| steelhead rainbow trout on spawning run | 4/18 | Willoughby Falls | 46° overcast, north breeze, ready to rain | started today (lasts 10 days) |
| spring peepers | 4/28 | marsh where great blue heron fishes | 41° sunny with cold north wind | |

## activity 2

### BECOME A CITIZEN SCIENTIST

"Journey North" and "Project Budburst" are programs that collect phenology observations from people around the country. Their materials and websites describe what to look for and when and how. Maps are updated with each participant's entry, displaying the seasons as they advance north and south throughout the year. The USA National Phenology Network (www.usanpn.org) is a good resource for scientific information and current research, especially the effect that climate change is having on nature's seasonal calendar.

## activity 3

GO ON A "SPRING ARRIVES" ALPHABET HUNT

Look and listen for these migrators and emergers from early to late spring. Consider bringing along an explorer's kit with a magnifying glass, sketchpad, colored pencils, binoculars, and a shallow white bucket for looking at pond water.

**A** American toads trilling or ants
**B** black flies or bumble bees or bats or buds or blossoms
**C** caterpillar or chipmunk
**D** dandelions or daddy longlegs or deer with new fawn
**E** ermine molting or earthworm
**F** fiddleheads or flowering trees
**G** garter snake sunning or geese honking northward
**H** hawk or hermit thrush or hepatica
**I** ice-out (compare a local stream, brook, pond, and lake)
**J** jack-in-the-pulpit or jelly fungus (look for new growth on old fungi)
**K** killdeer or kits playing
**L** loon or wild leeks or lady's slippers
**M** mourning cloak butterfly or monarch butterfly or morel
**N** newt or nest with eggs or noisy nestlings
**O** ovenbird (listen for "teacher Teacher TEACHER") or osprey
**P** pussy willows or painted lady butterfly or pine pollen falling in waves
**Q** paper wasp queen building her nest
**R** red-winged blackbird or robin
**S** spring peepers or salamanders
**T** trillium or turtle or tadpoles
**U** urine scent marking (fox urine smells strongly of skunk in very early spring)
**V** vernal pool or violets or vireo
**W** wood frog eggs or woodcock peenting
**X** xylem awakening (drink some fresh sap or syrup)
**Y** yellow-bellied sapsucker drilling or yellow birch growth tasting like wintergreen
**Z** zooplankton (look in a bucket of water from a pond or vernal pool for mosquito and midge larvae, rotifers, and poppy-size water fleas)

# Old Logs Take on New Life

Examining a decaying log up-close can reveal a surprising diversity of life. What you find on your log will depend on its species, habitat, and stage of decomposition. You might observe certain plants, animals, and fungi on one log that are not present on another one nearby.

If you can, visit your log several times each season. Over time you will observe the succession of organisms that use it, and watch it decay. It may take a decade or more to fully decompose!

## activity 1

### AT FIRST GLANCE

**Materials**:

identification guides

flashlight

**Procedure**:

1. Notice the amount of decay the log has gone through. Is it still round, with peeling bark that can be pulled off (early stage of decay), or can you pull off large chunks of softened wood that no longer have bark (middle stage of decay)? Are there woodpecker or insect holes on the bark? Is algae growing on it? Can you smell the earthy scent of decay?
2. Look at the plants growing on the log. Can you find ferns, mosses, lichen, mushrooms, or wildflowers? Has the log become a nursery for a growing seedling? What else do you see?
3. Look for animals. Can you find beetles, termites, salamanders, insect larvae, snails, slugs, or daddy longlegs? What else do you see?
4. Look for evidence of animals that were once there. Are there little nests that a mouse made? Is there a pile of midden left by a squirrel where he perched on the log for a snack? Did a snake shed its skin here? What else do you see?
5. Did an animal dig out a shelter in the end of the log? Use the flashlight to look inside any deep holes.
6. Carefully roll the log over just far enough to observe the bottom of the log and the ground under it. Is there any slime mold growing? Do you see ants scurrying around? This part of the log is becoming part of the soil. Are there earthworms beneath it? What else do you see? Return the log to its original position when you are finished looking.
7. Think about the rotting log as an ecosystem. How is it used for food and shelter? How do the organisms on the log interact with the log and with each other?

## activity 2

### GETTING CLOSER

**Materials**:

magnifying lens

pocketknife or small trowel

**Procedure**:

1. Pull aside some of the loose bark. Look at the underside of the bark. Look at the layer of log beneath the bark. Can you see where beetles bored holes and formed tunnels? Are there sow bugs or millipedes? What else do you see?
2. Can you find any frass? Frass is scat or debris left by chewing insects. It may look like sawdust or fine wood chips.
3. Examine it with your magnifying lens.
4. Use the lens to find teeth marks, miniature skeletons, pupa cases, and other tiny evidence of plant and animal life.
5. Use the pocketknife or trowel to dig into crevices in your search for living things.

# activity 3

## BRINGING THINGS HOME

**Field Materials**:
bug bottle(s)
gloves or blunt tweezers
cup of water in a bottle or jar
small container to carry a sample of algae

**Home Materials**:
microscope
flat microscope slide
medicine dropper
microscope slide with a droplet well
sharp knife
identification guides and other sources of information

**Preparation**:
Steps 1-3 are in the field.
Steps 4-6 are at home.
Be prepared to return any creatures to the same log you got them from.

**Procedure**:
1. Carefully place any small animals or plants you want to study or identify into the bug bottle(s). Include some of the log material you found them on. Handle critters with gloves or tweezers.
2. Select a handful of the dampest parts of the rotting wood. Include some moss or lichen if you can. Add it to the cup of water.
3. Place a small sample of moist algae in the container.
4. Study the specimens. Use identification guides and materials to learn more about them.
5. Briskly stir the mixture of water and wood, then let it settle. (Or mash it as Bill Amos described in the related essay in this book.) Place a few drops of the murky water into the slide's well. Observe with a microscope. Do you see tiny organisms swimming around? You just might find a moss piglet (water bear) or protozoan secretly using your log as its home.
6. Add a drop of water to the algae if it is not already damp. Snip a small bit to place on a flat slide. Use the tip of a sharp knife to separate and smear the algae into thin sections on the slide. Use your microscope to study the plant cells.

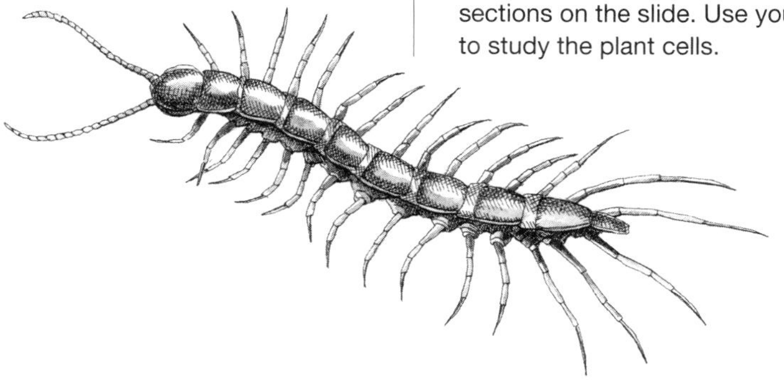

# Butterflies at the Bar

Whether you already have butterflies visiting your yard or want to attract a few for the first time, these three projects will invite them to come and linger a while. Have your binoculars handy!

## activity 1
### MAKE A PUDDLING POOL

**Materials**:

shallow container, such as a garbage can cover or aluminum roasting pan

sand or dirt (enough to fill the pan to within one-half inch of the rim)

one gallon of water in a jug or bucket with one tablespoon table salt added (additional salted water may be needed, depending on the size of the container)

trowel or heavy wooden spoon

**Preparation**:

Locate a sunny, open spot to place the puddling pool. A good place to start is near some bright flowers. Try to place it where you can observe from a distance.

**Procedure**:

1. Take the materials to the site where you are going to make the puddling pool.
2. Fill the container with sand or dirt.
3. Slowly pour the water onto the sand.
4. Use the trowel or wooden spoon to thoroughly mix the water and sand. The sand should be saturated, with some standing water visible on the surface.
5. From afar, watch for butterflies sipping the mineral-laden water. With binoculars, you might be able to see their proboscises unfurling.
6. If lack of rain or dew causes the sand to dry up, add more water but not more salt. While the water evaporated (or was sipped), most of the salt remained in the sand.

Investigate how butterflies react to *different levels of salinity*. To test this, prepare two additional puddling pools using water with increased amounts of salt, say three tablespoons and six tablespoons. Do butterflies visit one pool more than the other two? To discover if there is a level at which the saltiness deters butterflies, add increasingly saltier water over a few days' time to one of the pools.

# activity 2

MAKE A FRUIT FEEDER

**Materials**:

the rind from a cleaned-out grapefruit or orange half

heavy screwdriver or other means of punching holes in the rind

three 12-inch pieces of string or yarn

juicy, over-ripe fruit such as watermelon, strawberries, bananas, peaches, orange halves, or apple wedges

**Procedure**:

1. Punch three holes evenly spaced around the cut edge of the rind, about one inch below the edge.
2. Attach a string to each hole, tying a secure knot. Pull the three strings together up above the center of the rind and tie them in a single knot. Your rind can now be hung from a branch or hook.
3. Fill the rind with pieces of fruit. Experiment to see what your local butterflies are attracted to.
4. Hang the feeder out of the sun. It won't last a long time, but can easily be replaced the next time you have citrus for breakfast!

# activity 3

MAKE A SPONGE SIPPER

**Materials**:

new kitchen sponge – purple or pink attracts many types of butterflies

scissors to cut sponge

plastic container with tight-fitting lid, such as a yogurt cup or butter tub

razor blade or X-Acto knife to cut lid

sugar

small cupboard hook, string

purple or pink duct tape (optional)

**Procedure**:

1. Bring one-half cup of water to a boil. Remove from heat. Add two tablespoons sugar. Stir until sugar dissolves completely. Set aside to cool.
2. Cut a one-inch-wide piece from the long side of the sponge.
3. Cut a small rectangular slot near the center of the plastic lid. Make it slightly smaller than the sponge so that the sponge fits in snugly.
4. Push one end of the sponge down through the slot from the top side of the lid. Leave two inches sticking out of the top.
5. Screw the hook into the center of the outside bottom of the container.
6. Cover the container and lid with colorful tape, if desired.
7. Wet the entire sponge with water to puff it up. Squeeze out the water so the sponge is moist but not dripping.
8. Pour the cooled sugar solution into the container.
9. Dip the top section of the sponge into the solution to moisten it.
10. Snap the lid onto the container.
11. Turn the container upside down. Use the string to hang it by the hook.
12. Every few days rinse off the sponge and replace the sugar water.

# Ground Beetles: In a Pitfall Trap Near You

Once you start paying attention to beetles, you'll be amazed by how many kinds can inhabit even a small patch of land. Kids, especially, are fascinated by these hardy insects.

## activity 1

MAKE A PITFALL TRAP

**Materials**:

trowel or small shovel to dig soil

large container (yogurt cup, coffee can, etc.)

four stones about the same size, one-half to one inch in height

handful of leaf litter

piece of board that is several inches larger than the top of the container

**Procedure**:

1. Dig a hole the same size as the container.
2. Set the container snugly in the hole so its rim is level with the ground.
3. Place a handful of leaf litter in the bottom of the container for the trapped critters to burrow into.
4. Place the board over the container, supported by the four stones. Beetles and other nocturnal creatures will be attracted to the darkness under the board and fall into the trap. The board also keeps rain and debris out, keeps large critters from crawling in, and keeps birds from eating the trapped insects.
5. Leave the pitfall trap set up overnight.
6. Check it in the morning to see what was wandering around during the night.

   *Note: some ground beetles can leave an irritating chemical on your fingers; handle with caution.*
7. Experiment with pitfall traps in different habitats: lawn, forest edge, woods, near the house, or in a garden, for example.

# activity 2

OBSERVE BURYING BEETLES

**Materials**:

large container (yogurt cup, coffee can, etc.) with the bottom cut out and removed

carrion bait, such as a dead mouse or a rodent-sized piece of meat

**Procedure**:

1. Follow the instructions in Activity One to make a pitfall trap, but remove the bottom of the container for this activity.

2. Set the container snugly in the hole so its rim is level with the ground.

3. Place the bait on the ground at the bottom of the container. Set the board above the container, supported by the stones.

4. Leave the pitfall trap in place overnight. In the morning you might find burying beetles excavating a hole under the bait. The carcass becomes home for their eggs and food for their young.

5. Once burying beetles have inhabited your pitfall trap, remove the container and put back the board to allow them an unconfined environment to raise their young.

# Keep Forests Beautiful: Litter

A walk through the autumn woods kicks up more than just a wonderfully earthy smell. It literally rearranges the habitat of hundreds of tiny organisms hidden in the fallen leaves. At the hands-and-knees level, you can discover some of the smaller species that live in, and sometimes help create, the leaf litter.

## activity 1

### WHAT'S IN LEAF LITTER?

**Materials**:

12-foot piece of string

large light-colored ground cloth (tarp, old sheet, etc.)

magnifying glass

flashlight

field guide for invertebrates (optional)

**Procedure**:

1. Find an area of the forest where there is a four- to five-inch layer of leaves on the ground.
2. Lay the string on the ground so that it forms a three-foot square around the spot you have chosen.
3. Open the ground cloth next to the square.
4. Look at the top layer of leaves and debris.
   What kind of leaves are they?
   What condition are they in?
   Are they dry?
   Are they mostly whole?
   What do you see besides leaves?
   Are there any pieces of bark?
   Twigs?
   Any plants?
   Nuts or seeds?
5. Move the top layer of leaves to a corner of the ground cloth and spread it out. Examine it for creatures you didn't see at first. Beetles, spiders, and harvestmen (often called daddy longlegs) are commonly found in the upper layers of woodland litter. In a moist forest you might see a red eft feeding on tiny prey.
6. Look at the next layer in your square. Do the leaves look more decayed than the top layer? They might be softer, moister, or skeletonized. Carefully move this layer to a different part of the ground cloth and spread it out. Many critters contribute to the decay of this middle section of litter: ants, insects, sowbugs, pseudoscorpions, flies, and centipedes are commonly found.
7. Continue to remove layers of leaves and set them on different sections of the ground cloth to examine. Use your magnifying glass to study leaf bits and tiny animals. Notice how leaves at the bottom of the forest litter are even more decayed than the leaves from the middle layers: soggier, darker, and more easily torn.
8. Mites and springtails are the most common inhabitants of leaf litter in a deciduous forest. Look closely for these tiny arthropods. Throughout the decaying leaves you might see a lacy web of white or yellow threads that are part of the fungi that break down woody material. The slime found on most of the leaves (or bits of leaves) in the bottom layer is caused by bacteria that are decomposing the leaf into soluble nutrients.
9. When all of the leaves are on the ground cloth, examine the bare ground. You might see earthworms, millipedes, slugs, snails, fly larvae, and more springtails. Shine the flashlight to highlight dark critters camouflaged against the soil.
10. Return the leaf litter back to the forest floor, starting with the bottom layer. Rebuild the leaf litter pile as naturally as possible. Remove the string.

# activity 2

## HOW LONG CAN DECAY TAKE?

This activity works best in early autumn as trees are beginning to display fall colors.

**Materials**:

one green leaf from each of four or five trees of different species

tree netting or wire mesh, large enough to cover all of the leaves (one-inch openings work well)

garden-fabric staples or other means of securing the netting to the ground

journal or camera (optional)

**Preparation**:

Select a mostly shaded spot in your yard where the netting can be left on the ground for an extended period of time.

**Procedure**:

1. Lay the leaves next to each other on the ground.
2. Place the netting on top of the leaves and secure it with fabric staples.
3. Take a photo or draw a sketch of the leaf array. Write down the date and the name and placement of each leaf.
4. Observe the leaves throughout the fall season. They will be walked on, bitten into, softened with rain, broken down by a myriad of invertebrates, and eventually decomposed by microscopic bacteria, fungi, and protozoa.
5. Document the changes every few days. In what order did the leaves decay? How long did the process take?

# Woolly Bears: Forecast Flops?

Woolly bear caterpillars are fun to collect and observe. Look for them prowling across fields, lawns, and roads just about the time of the first frost.

## activity 1
### COLLECTING WOOLLY BEARS

**Materials**:

container with lid that has holes in it

green plants, especially grass and clover; pieces of maple or birch leaves

water to moisten food plants

optional: large plastic spoon (handling the caterpillar gently is fine, but if you don't wish to touch it, scoop it up with the spoon)

**Procedure**:

1. Place the plants in the bottom of the container. If you are going to overwinter the caterpillar, insert a twig that is long enough to lean against the side of the container.
2. Gently drop the caterpillar onto the plants. If it curled up in your hand, it will open up within a few minutes.
3. If the woolly bear is on a leaf or twig, put them together into the container.
4. Feed your caterpillar some of the same material you found it on. Give it fresh grass every day. Other plants can also be added, but grass is necessary. Moisten the plants slightly before putting them in the container.
5. Replace the lid and give the caterpillar at least a half-hour to rest before you handle it in the following activities.

## activity 2
### OBSERVING WOOLLY BEARS

**Materials**:

paper to place caterpillars on: 12x18 inches is a good size, white or cream-colored highlights the caterpillars well (and displays any frass they leave – also good to study)

bits of fruit, such as apple or pumpkin

ruler, calculator, stopwatch, pencil

**Procedure**:

1. Gently place the caterpillar on the paper.
2. Examine the bands of orange and black. Based on your observation, do you think your woolly bear is predicting an easy winter or a hard one? What kind of spring and summer do you think this woolly bear experienced?
3. Use the ruler to measure the three bands. If you have more than one caterpillar, can you tell which one is oldest, youngest? (Hint: as woolly bears grow, black setae are replaced with orange ones.) Calculate the ratio of each band to the other two. If you have more than one caterpillar, can you determine an average band size?
4. Predict how long you think it takes a woolly bear caterpillar to cross the length of the paper. Draw starting and finishing lines for a race if you have more than one caterpillar. Gently place the caterpillar on one edge and watch it move. Does it travel in a straight line? Does having bits of fruit at the other end make a difference in the direction or speed that the caterpillar travels?

# activity 3

## OBSERVING HIBERNATION

**Materials**:

container with lid that has holes in it

moistened food plants

twig that is long enough to lean against the side of the container

**Preparation**:

Locate a protected place to keep the container outside during the winter, for example, underneath a deck. The container must stay as cold as the outdoors, but be protected from snow and wind.

**Procedure**:

1. Continue to feed your caterpillar various food plants, especially grass.
2. Clean out the container every few days. Dispose of waste and dried plants. Wash the sides of the container.
3. When the caterpillar appears sluggish and stops eating, place a small amount of fresh grass loosely in the container. Place the container in a cold spot where you can observe the caterpillar bury itself under the top layer of plants.
4. When the caterpillar has hibernated, place the container in the spot you have chosen to protect it for the winter.
5. Next spring when weeds start to green up and dandelions appear, bring the container into the warm air but not in direct sunshine. Watch for the caterpillar to emerge from hibernation.
6. Place the caterpillar on a pile of grass while you clean out the container and fill it with fresh greens. Put the caterpillar back in. The woolly bear will eat ravenously for a few days. Clean the container every day.
7. Watch for it to spin a cocoon on the twig (or maybe the side of the container). Keep the container in a warm spot with lots of air but not direct sunshine (so it does not heat up too much).
8. In a week or two the cocoon will open and a lovely yellow tiger moth will emerge. Release it shortly after taking pictures and oohing and aahing.

# Goldenrod: The Everything, Everywhere Flower

Goldenrods are an important part of a local ecosystem. Visit these sunny flowers to see how insects make themselves right at home.

## activity 1
### GETTING TO KNOW GOLDENRODS

**Materials**:
hand lens or magnifying glass
quart-size clear storage bag
wildflower field guide (optional)

**Procedure**:
1. Find a patch of goldenrods. Can you find more than one species? There are many kinds of goldenrods native to the Northeast. Notice the shape of the flower heads, the individual flowers on a stalk, whether the stems are hairy or smooth, and the variety of yellows on display.
2. Carefully inspect an individual plant, searching it from base to flower. How many creatures can you find inhabiting this plant?
3. Wrap the clear bag around a flower head. Turn it upside down and shake hard. Notice that pollen does not come off into the bag. Goldenrod pollen is heavy and sticky – proof that it cannot cause hay fever attacks!
4. Grasp the flower and rub it firmly between your fingers. Did you get some of the sticky pollen on your fingers? There might be yellow on your fingers, too; goldenrod flowers make a beautiful yellow dye.
5. Look at the plant stem for galls. Round *ball galls* are made by the goldenrod gall fly. Spindle-shaped *elliptical galls* are made by the goldenrod gall moth. Look at the tip of the plant for a bunch or rosette gall, which appears as a tight cluster of leaves and is made by a midge (a type of tiny fly). Which type of gall seems most common in your patch? Is there more than one gall on any of the goldenrods? If so, are they the same type of gall?

# activity 2

## INVESTIGATING BALL AND ELLIPTICAL GALLS

**Materials**:

ball and/or elliptical goldenrod galls

penknife

hand lens or magnifying glass

small freezer-safe cup

masking tape

large jar, cheesecloth, or fine mesh screen

flashlight

**Preparation**:

Collect ball and elliptical goldenrod galls by cutting the plant stems a few inches above and below each gall.

**Procedure**:

Look closely at each gall.
What kind of gall is it?
Do you see a hole, or is the gall intact?

**If there is a hole**:

1. Look at its size and condition. A tiny hole is a sign that the insect has emerged. This will likely appear on the side of a ball gall, and near the top of an elliptical gall. A larger or ragged hole would indicate that a predator, such as a downy woodpecker or chickadee, pecked its way in for a meal.
2. Cut the gall in half vertically. Look at the nutrient chamber, which is pithy in the ball gall and silky smooth in the elliptical gall.
3. Do you see an exit tunnel leading to the hole in the gall? Does it appear to be old or new? Gall fly larvae prepare tunnels in fall, and use them in spring, when they emerge as adult insects. Gall moth larvae form exit tunnels in late summer and emerge in the fall.

**If there is not a hole:**

1. Use the hand lens to examine the gall's surface. Look for a thin spot that covers an exit tunnel in a ball gall, or a mix of silk and flower parts covering an exit hole in an elliptical gall (this was prepared by the moth larva, before retreating into the gall to pupate). Note: depending on the coloring and condition of an individual gall, this is not always possible to find.
2. Carefully cut a long vertical slit in the gall, but do not cut into the center of the gall, where the insect may be pupating.
3. Using the knife or your fingers, pry open the gall, so that the center is revealed. In many cases, it will be necessary to pull the gall apart into two approximate halves.
4. If you find a white larva inside a ball gall, carefully place it in your warm hand. It will slowly become active and start moving around. You can place it in a cup in the freezer for a few hours, then take it out and watch it warm up and wiggle again. Take a look at it under your hand lens.
5. Other creatures may also be found inside the gall. Sometimes the adult fly dies before it can emerge. Or you might find bees, wasps, beetles, ants, or other larvae or pupae. Sometimes both the rightful inhabitant *and* a predator or parasite are found together.
6. Once any larvae are removed from the center of the gall, you may be able to use your flashlight to find the exit tunnel. Shine the flashlight at close range on the inside of each half of the gall and look on the opposite, outside surface side for a pinprick of light.
7. To return the insect to the outdoors, close the gall with masking tape (not Scotch tape) and place it in a shady spot. Be sure not to cover up the thin spot/plugged exit hole with the tape.
8. You can keep an unopened gall in a jar covered with cheesecloth. Place it out of the sun and away from heat. Depending on the type of gall, a moth will emerge in autumn or a fly the next spring. Release it outdoors to continue its short life.

# Pine on the Cob

As if they needed any more encouragement, red squirrels (and others) have their own special day: January 21 is National Squirrel Appreciation Day. The timing is appropriate, as red squirrels are active all winter, leaving behind many signs of their presence. In winter look for them near mid-day; in warmer seasons they are most active in the early morning and late afternoon.

## activity 1

### LOOKING FOR SQUIRREL SIGN

Look for the following red squirrel sign. Because other animals make very similar signs (except for their distinctive middens and unique noises), the more of these you find, the more confident you can be that you are standing in red squirrel territory.

Binoculars are handy for looking at treetop nests. A magnifying glass to examine bite marks is helpful but not necessary.

**Middens**: These are piles of dry cones, discarded cone scales, empty cone cores, green cones (especially deep inside the pile), and occasionally nuts. Large middens usually accumulate at the base of a coniferous tree. Smaller middens are often present near the opening of a nest hole or ground burrow. A male red squirrel defends four to five acres of forest; the largest midden is often near the center of his territory.

**Mushrooms**: Red squirrels hang mushrooms from tree branches to dry them for later use. They also stick them in the crotches of trees, as they more frequently do with apples and cones.

**Hemlock twigs**: Small twigs scattered on the ground beneath a hemlock tree, with their cones and buds bitten off, may be a sign of red squirrel feeding. Look with a magnifying glass to see the typical rodent bite: clean and slanted. Other rodents, such as porcupines, also do this to tree tips, but red squirrels in particular favor hemlock.

**Drey**: A drey is a large, compact nest built high up in a coniferous tree near the trunk. It is made of leaves, many strips of shredded bark, and fibrous materials such as grapevine. A series of dreys is often built in neighboring trees, allowing the squirrel to run and jump from one to another. These are used for raising young and for summer shelter.

**Nest holes**: Red squirrels sometimes nest in tree cavities, especially in the winter. Holes dug in the ground, 2.5 to 3 inches across, are also used. Protected spaces in stone walls make good sites, too. Nests are lined with soft shredded bark, dry grasses, and other fibrous material.

**Ground burrow**: A system of tunnels connects a ground burrow with feeding sites. A pile of cone scales marks the entrance. Three-inch-wide tunnels are made in winter if the snow is six or more inches deep.

**Tapped trees**: Red squirrels bite the bark of many hardwood trees, especially red and sugar maple, then return to lap up the "syrup" that is produced after several hours of the sap evaporating. Other birds and animals have this habit, too; use a magnifying glass to look for the red squirrel's tiny bite marks near oozing sap. The bite has two parts and looks a bit like a sideways exclamation point.

**Noises**: Many noises distinguish a red squirrel from other forest inhabitants. Loud, persistent chatters, trills, squeaks, and chirps are but a few of their vocalizations. When you are walking in the woods, a squirrel's scolding is often your first clue of its presence.

# activity 2

FOOD PREFERENCES

**Materials**:
a variety of foods that red squirrels like, such as wild berries, unsalted peanuts, sunflower seeds, dried corn, apple chunks, acorns, beechnuts, or hazelnuts

**Preparation**:
Locate a habitat where red squirrels are seen frequently, either in the woods, in a park, or at home.

**Procedure**:
1. Measure one cup each of three or four foods to test.
2. Place each food in a separate pile, about six inches apart, on a deck railing, a board on the ground, or a large rock.
3. Watch to see which pile the squirrels take from most often. If you can watch for long enough, or enough times in the same place, you will begin to recognize individual squirrels. Determine whether each has its own preferences.
4. Which foods do the squirrels take away to eat near a tree or to cache for later? Which foods do they eat immediately at the "table?" (The answer depends partly on the season. They are more likely to store food in the fall but eat it right away in the winter.)
5. If you can, perform this experiment both at home and in the forest. Is there a difference in which foods are preferred and how they are eaten, comparing the woods to a residential setting?

# activity 3

ACROBATIC SKILLS

**Materials**:
three pine cones smeared with peanut butter

three peanuts in the shell

rope, 12 to 16 feet long

six pieces of twine, about 10 inches long

**Preparation**:
Find two trees that are five to six feet apart.

**Procedure**:
1. Tie the rope like a tightrope about five feet high between the trees.
2. Use the twine to attach the cones and peanuts alternately to the rope, spaced evenly apart.
3. Observe how nimble and agile the red squirrels are as they walk along the rope and interact with the cones and peanuts. Notice how they use their tails to balance themselves in any position. (Falls do happen, though, which is why you won't want to do this over pavement or very hard ground.) Appreciate their contortions as they work to get at the food.
4. One kind of food is much larger than the other. Does the squirrel use different strategies for freeing and/or eating it?

# Catch a Falling Snowflake

Snowflakes of all shapes and sizes are fun to compare. You can catch tiny frozen needles, fat lacy dendrites, and lots of pretty parts that have broken off in the fall to earth. Try collecting and melting different types of snow to compare how much water they each make.

## activity 1

### OBSERVING SNOWFLAKES

**Materials**:

black cloth or construction paper

magnifying glass or hand lens

**Preparation**:

Keep the cloth or construction paper in the freezer.

Plan where you are going to study your snowflakes – a place out of the falling snow but cold enough to prevent melting. A garage or covered deck works great.

**Procedure**:

1. Carry the cloth or paper outside to catch falling snow.
2. When the paper is about three-fourths covered, bring it to your sheltered spot.
3. Use the lens to study your snowflakes.

## activity 2

### MEASURING MELTED SNOW

**Materials**:

three or four identical cans

scoop or small shovel

measuring cup

masking tape and marker, or some way to label the cans when filled with snow

**Preparation**:

Locate areas with different types of snow: fresh-fallen snow in the yard, snow from a plowed pile, snow fallen off the roof, old snow (underneath the fresh snow, perhaps), etc.

**Procedure**:

1. Use the scoop or shovel to fill each can with a different type of snow. Label each can as you go so you can remember what type of snow is in each can. Do not pack the snow, just scoop and drop it in the can without changing how tightly packed or dense the snow naturally is.
2. Inside, place the cans in the sink or in a bucket.
3. After the snow has melted, pour out and measure the amount of water each can of snow produced. Did the new snow produce more water or less water than the old or packed snow? Can you figure out why?

# activity 3

## PRESERVING SNOWFLAKES ON A MICROSCOPE SLIDE

**Materials**:

glass microscope slide

thin permanent marker (optional)

can of clear acrylic spray

gloves that allow you to hold the slide easily

microscope

**Preparation**:

Use a thin permanent marker to draw a small star (or snowflake!) in the bottom left-hand corner of a clean slide. This will help you know which side is up without having to touch the delicate surface once it has snowflakes on it.

Place the slide in the freezer. Laying it in a small jewelry box will help you find it in a hurry and protect it from breaking.

Keep the can of acrylic spray in the refrigerator door. (Acrylic spray is available at hardware and craft stores.)

Place a pair of gloves where you can grab them quickly.

Plan where you are going to let your snowflakes set into the spray. The slide will need a couple of hours in a cold, sheltered spot in order to set.

**Procedure**:

1. Be dressed and ready to go outside – you will want to get outside quickly with your frozen slide, before it warms up!
2. Remove the can of spray from the refrigerator. Keeping the door open (to form a cool space to work), remove the cap and shake the can.
3. Remove the slide from the freezer. In the cool protection of the refrigerator door, spray the slide to cover one surface.
4. Shut the refrigerator door and dash outside with the slide.
5. Hold the slide in the falling snow or lay it on a surface such as a deck railing. Watch to see that it doesn't become completely covered or you will not be able to see individual snowflakes under the microscope. About half or three-fourths full is good.
6. When you have enough flakes, or you have captured a particularly spectacular specimen, take the slide to your cold, sheltered spot. Leave it there for at least two hours.
7. Bring the slide in when it is dry. Place it under a microscope. See how many different types of snowflakes you collected. Your slide will be a permanent record of that snowfall; consider writing the date along one edge.
8. Experiment with different types of snow in other storms.

# Buds: Spanning the Seasons

We don't usually pay much attention to trees during the winter, except for admiring the beauty of their silhouettes. Here are some ways to appreciate the life that is hiding inside tree buds during the coldest time of year. Activity One can take place all winter. Begin Activity Two after trees have been dormant; early February is a safe bet. The end of sugaring season is a great time to do Activity Three.

## activity 1

### BUDS ON A TREE

**Materials**:

two eight-inch pieces of brightly colored string

magnifying glass

**Procedure**:

1. Find a tree that you can visit easily throughout the winter.
2. Locate two terminal buds (at the ends of branches) that are within easy reach.
3. Tie a string below the closest lateral (side) bud. Wrap it several times and tie it twice to keep the wind and birds from snatching it away. The strings will help you find your buds each time you visit.
4. Observe details about the buds and twigs.
5. Return every few weeks throughout the winter. Start visiting every few days when the buds begin to change in size or color. Check every day, if possible, as they get fatter near the end of winter.
6. When the buds puff up and look like they are about to pop open, snip one off to use in Activity Three. Keep the string on the twig; the lateral bud should keep it from sliding off the branch.
7. Keep watching the remaining bud until it bursts open. Don't remove the string yet. How many weeks did you observe this bud? Is it the first bud to open on this tree? Did it contain a leaf or a flower?
8. Throughout spring, enjoy watching the leaf or flower grow into full size and color. Also watch the twig where you removed the bud. How does the tree adapt to the loss of this bud?

## activity 2

### BUDS UNDER A MAGNIFYING GLASS MICROSCOPE SLIDE

**Materials**:

large unopened buds from different trees

sharp knife or razor blade

magnifying glass

tweezers

**Procedure**:

1. Examine the scales on the outside of each bud. They protect the tender new plant. What color are they? Rub them; are they smooth, rough, sticky, crispy? Are they split open a bit? Use the magnifying glass to observe minute details. Do you see any hairs?
2. Consider what you will find inside each bud. A leaf? A flower? Both?
3. Carefully slice through the outside of a bud lengthwise. Open it up. Examine the interior of the bud with the magnifying glass.
4. Pull out the leaf (or flower) with the tweezers. Notice how it comes out: Was it folded in half? Pleated neatly? Rolled up at the edges? Scrunched into a wad? Each tree has its own unique bud shape and internal leaf arrangement.

# activity 3
## BUDS IN A JAR

**Materials**:
clippers or pruners, bucket with three to four inches of water, masking tape, pen

four jars filled with two to three inches of lukewarm water

hammer

four index cards, pen

**Preparation**:
Select four or five trees from which you can clip several twigs. Good choices are sugar maple, red maple, yellow birch, white birch, quaking aspen, white ash, red oak, cherry, wild apple, and willow.

Locate four dissimilar places in your house to keep a jar of water and twigs for an extended period of time: a sunny south windowsill, a spot with good natural light but not direct sunlight, a dark space such as a closet, and a cold spot such as the refrigerator (the bottom shelf in the door works well). Label each jar with its intended location.

Prepare four masking tape labels for each tree. These will go around the twigs as you collect them. Stick your labels along the brim of the bucket to carry them into the field. (Labels can be made outside if you aren't sure which trees you will use until you go out, though this is not as pleasant to do in the cold.)

**Procedure**:
1. Clip four twigs, about 10 inches long, from each tree. Be sure to include a terminal bud and several lateral buds on each twig.
2. Secure a masking tape label around each twig. Keep the labeled twigs in the bucket of water.
3. At home, clip off the bottom half-inch of a twig. Smash the end gently with the hammer to improve water absorption. Immediately place the twig in one of the jars of lukewarm water. Repeat this procedure with every twig. Each jar should have a twig from each type of tree.
4. Place the jars of twigs in their designated locations. List the trees and jar location on each index card; keep one card with each jar. As a twig opens its first bud, record the date on the card.
5. Every five days, rinse the bottoms of the twigs and put fresh water into the jars.
6. Continue this experiment for six weeks.
7. Move all four jars to the sunny windowsill. Continue to record the date that the rest of the twigs open their first bud. Which jar has all of its twigs leaf out first? Last? In what order (generally) did the trees leaf out? Did you get any flowers, or were they all leaves? Did any buds have both?
8. What can you conclude about how light and temperature affect bud burst?

# Further Resources for Environmental Education

Are you interested in exploring more environmental education opportunities, for classroom or informal learning? Although a full listing of resources is beyond the scope of this book, below are some recommended links to get you started. We also encourage you to check out the rich archive of articles available on the Northern Woodlands website (northernwoodlands.org) and in particular, the full *Outside Story* series (northernwoodlands.org/outside_story).

Please note, as well, that there are likely to be good resources in your area that you can access with just a little research. For example, is there a local biologist, forester, or naturalist who would be willing to talk to your class or group, or perhaps join you for a walk in the woods? Perhaps there's a conservation commission, land trust, or woodland owners association that holds outdoor events. Your state's fish and wildlife department, forestry department, and park and recreation department (titles vary by state), are also great places to start; they have a number of highly knowledgeable people on staff, and are actively engaged in public education.

In addition to the general list of organizations below, we'd be remiss not mentioning two outstanding educators who served as early sounding boards for this appendix (but who did not review the text, and aren't responsible for typos). Special thanks to Hannah Putnam at the Vermont Institute of Natural Science and Lisa Purcell at Four Winds Nature Institute.

Here are their organizations' websites. Check them out:

Four Winds Nature Institute .......... fwni.org
Vermont Institute of Natural Science .......... vinsweb.org

And if you're in the Upper Valley of New Hampshire and Vermont, be sure to check out the site for New Hampshire Charitable Foundation's Wellborn Ecology Fund (nhcf.org/wellborn), which includes information about grants to support ecology education, gatherings for educators, professional development opportunities for educators who work in the Upper Valley region, and other information.

## Helpful General Resources

Association for Science Teacher Education .......... theaste.org
New England Environmental Education Alliance .......... neeea.org
North American Association for Environmental Education .......... naaee.org
Project Learning Tree .......... plt.org
Project WET .......... projectwet.org
Project Wild .......... projectwild.org

# About the Authors

BILL AMOS, a former marine biologist, metamorphosed over the years into an author, bio-photographer, and naturalist who found every aspect of the living world fascinating. His publications include more than a dozen books, articles for *National Geographic*, *Scientific American*, *Reader's Digest*, and other magazines, and newspaper columns. He and his wife, Catherine, occupied what was once a hillside farm in Vermont's Northeast Kingdom.

VIRGINIA BARLOW worked for many years at Redstart Forestry, which she started in 1992. She's worked for *Northern Woodlands* since its beginning, mostly editing and doing a little writing. She's been on a number of boards and committees, both in Corinth, Vermont, and for Vermont statewide organizations

MADELINE BODIN has been writing about the environment for over 20 years. She specializes in wildlife and ecology, and seeks to tell a good story. Madeline lives in southern Vermont.

WILLIS "KUBIE" BROWN graduated Southern Vermont College in 2010 with a bachelor of arts in creative writing. Since that day, Willis has been doing his utter best to make sure he never has to work again. He spends his summers lost in the wilderness as a fly fishing and hunting guide in Montana, and his winters in Vermont, writing and living on the varied couches of his generous friends.

JOHN BUCK is a wildlife biologist with the Vermont Fish and Wildlife Department. He holds bachelor's and master's degrees in wildlife biology. During the past 36 years he has managed the White-tailed Deer Project, Nongame Bird Project, and managed private and public lands for wildlife habitat.

LEAH BURDICK lives in a cozy wood cabin with her favorite feline. After obtaining a master's degree in environmental science, she is now working on a law degree from Vermont Law School, concentrating on environmental social justice. When she isn't writing or studying the law, she can be found trying on sparkly costumes at her local dance studio, or wandering around the Upper Valley in search of really good ramen.

MICHAEL J. CADUTO is an international consultant in environmental education and stewardship, a storyteller, and singer-songwriter featured by NPR and the BBC. He is the award-winning author of 20 books, including the best-selling *Keepers of the Earth®* series (co-author), *Pond and Brook*, *Catch the Wind, Harness the Sun*, *Riparia's River*, and *Through a Naturalist's Eyes*. (www.p-e-a-c-e.net)

RUSS COHEN'S passionate avocation is connecting to nature via his taste buds. His book, *Wild Plants I Have Known...and Eaten*, was published in 2004 by the Essex County Greenbelt Association and is now in its sixth printing. Russ has been teaching foraging since 1974, and conducts over three dozen foraging walks and talks each year at a wide variety of venues throughout the Northeast. In addition, Russ is now aspiring to become a "Johnny Appleseed" of sorts for native edible plants: collecting wild edible seeds and nuts for propagating and planting, and assisting and partnering with others in this endeavor.

David Deen lives in Westminster, Vermont, and as the River Steward for the Connecticut River Watershed Council he is responsible for public education and advocacy. David has served in the Vermont Legislature for 28 years as chair of the Fish, Wildlife, and Water Resources Committee, among other assignments. He serves on the board of the Connecticut River chapter of Trout Unlimited and as an advisory committee member of the Vermont River Conservancy. He tries to fish whenever and wherever he can and represents fishing interests on the Vermont Connecticut River Resource Commission. David holds a MS in Environmental Science from Antioch New England Graduate School.

Celia Evans is an ecologist and educator. She lives in the Adirondacks of New York and teaches at Paul Smith's College. Celia is also a folk singer and songwriter.

Steven D. Faccio is a conservation biologist and co-founder of the Vermont Center for Ecostudies. Much of his work is focused on forest ecology, including long-term population monitoring of forest songbirds, ecology of pool-breeding amphibians, and vernal pool mapping and conservation. Steve is an avid backcountry skier, and enjoys hiking, fens, and live music.

Mary Holland is a naturalist, nature photographer, and author. She has written two books, *Naturally Curious* and *Naturally Curious Day by Day* (due out in fall 2016), as well as a number of children's books. She can usually be found exploring outside, photographing for her daily natural history blog, www.naturallycuriouswithmaryholland.wordpress.com. Mary is a collector of all things natural, from scat to skulls.

Charles W. Johnson is the former Vermont State Naturalist, a veteran of the U.S. Coast Guard, and author of several books, including *The Nature of Vermont*, *Bogs of the Northeast*, and, most recently, *Ice Ship*. Though widely traveled, he and his wife love exploring the "endless fascinations" in their hometown, East Montpelier, Vermont.

Howard Krum is a veterinarian, science writer, and author of the award-winning series "An Animal Life." He feels fortunate to live in Vermont and is surprised – on a daily basis – that his amazing wife, Mary Margaret, loves him.

Stephen Long is a co-founder and former editor of *Northern Woodlands* magazine. He is the author of *Thirty-Eight: The Hurricane that Transformed New England*, which chronicles the deadly hurricane's effect on forests and people.

Carolyn Lorié studied religion and philosophy at Mt. Holyoke College, but what she loves most are flowers and birds.

Barbara Mackay has been a Vermont educator for 40 years. As the daughter (and granddaughter and great-granddaughter) of foresters, she has enjoyed exploring and sharing nature with others since childhood. She secretly worries whether there is an age limit for building nature collections. Barb enjoys math, music, and any activity that gets her outside, especially hiking, snowshoeing, and camping in the mountains.

Dave Mance III is the editor of *Northern Woodlands* magazine.

ANNE MARGOLIS is a former writer and managing editor for *Northern Woodlands*, though she now develops and implements statewide renewable energy policies and programs for the State of Vermont. She lives in Corinth, Vermont, with her husband and daughter.

DECLAN MCCABE teaches biology at Saint Michael's College. His work with student researchers on insect communities in the Champlain Basin is funded by Vermont EPSCoR's Grant EPS-1101317 from the National Science Foundation.

KENT P. MCFARLAND is the co-founder of the Vermont Center for Ecostudies. He changes hats often – a wildlife biologist, conservation photographer, naturalist, writer, firefighter, runner, hiker, mountain biker, and dad. All of it rooted in the Green Mountains.

MEGHAN MCCARTHY MCPHAUL has been a horse-trekking guide in the west of Ireland, a ski shop manager in the mountains of Colorado, a soccer coach, waitress, and small town newspaper reporter. She spends lots of time wandering the mountains and woods of home, often with her faithful dog and three children, and her writing covers topics from ski history and land use to butterflies and bobcats. www.MeghanMcPhaul.com

BRIAN R. MITCHELL is an ecologist and adjunct assistant professor at the University of Vermont. He currently manages natural resource inventory and monitoring activities for national parks. He no longer gets much time to communicate with wild animals, except on days when the kids ingest too much sugar.

DIETLAND MÜLLER-SCHWARZE is professor emeritus at SUNY ESF, Syracuse. He studied scent communication in beavers, deer, muskrats, and reindeer, and authored several books. He grew up in the woodlands of Germany where he rock-climbed, and is an Adirondack Forty-Sixer. He likes to hike, snowshoe, travel the world, and graft apple trees.

MEGHAN OLIVER lives in Vermont.

LISA OLNEY is a writer and teacher who moved to the Upper Valley in 2009. Originally from Massachusetts, she lived in the southern Arizona desert for 12 years, but longed to return to her New England home. Lisa enjoys writing about a sense of place and people, and is inspired by the influence of folklore and how it relates to our natural world. She holds a BA in English from the University of Arizona and a M.Ed. in the Teaching of Writing from Plymouth State University.

BRYAN PFEIFFER, boy explorer, chases wildlife around the planet. He writes about nature and people, and teaches writing at the University of Vermont.

JOE RANKIN is a recovering newspaper journalist who's still trying to figure out what he wants to be when he grows up.

RACHEL MARIE SARGENT is a Vermonter and natural history enthusiast. She has written and illustrated for *Northern Woodlands*, taught science to kids at the California Academy of Sciences, and contributed to research at Harvard University. Rachel lives in Duxbury with her collection of orchids, two tanks of fish, and one husband.

SUSAN SHEA is a naturalist, conservation consultant, and freelance writer. For many years she acquired land and easements for the Green Mountain Club, protecting much of the Long Trail in northern Vermont. Susan is the former editor of GMC's membership magazine and has written for numerous publications.

LI SHEN is a retired biological researcher, conservationist, and sometime agitator.

STEVEN SHEPARD is the author of more than 70 books. An avid photographer, he can typically be found in the woods, lying in the mud, peering through his viewfinder. He lives in Williston, Vermont, with his wife Sabine, who has put up with him for more than 30 years.

TIFFANY SOUKUP is a world traveler, writer, and photographer. For a couple of summers, she called the 27,000-acre Groton State Forest her backyard where she was an innkeeper for Vermont State Parks. To find out what country Tiffany and her husband are currently living in, follow them at www.vagabondway.net.

NED SWANBERG is a floodplain and river corridor manager in Vermont. He loves picking through tide pools, walking in the White Mountains, and sauntering in the style of Henry Thoreau.

ELISE TILLINGHAST is the executive director of the Center for Northern Woodlands Education, and publisher of *Northern Woodlands* magazine.

TIM TRAVER is a native with roots in all the New England states, from the beaches of Buzzards Bay to the shores of Lake Champlain. A past director of the Norman Bird Sanctuary, the Upper Valley Land Trust, and The Vermont Institute of Natural Science, Tim is deeply inspired by the ever-changing cycles of field and forest around his home in Taftsville, Vermont, where he is particularly enthralled by his prairie garden. His book (Chelsea Green Publishing) *Sippewissett, or Life on a Salt Marsh*, explores the history of natural science on a Cape Cod salt marsh. His essays in *Lost in the Driftless: My Year of Fishing the Cultural Divide* (due out in Fall 2016) explore the conflicting cultural values of trout fishing in America.

KENRICK VEZINA is a renaissance man sans tights. He edits websites, writes essays, draws superheroes, and – when the need arises – pulls kids out of chest-deep muck in salt marshes. He is easily distracted by birds.

PATRICK WHITE is assistant editor of *Northern Woodlands* magazine, and along with his wife and son operates Meadow Ridge Christmas Tree Farm in Middlesex, Vermont.

MICHAEL WOJTECH is a freelancer who writes and teaches about trees – their identifying characteristics, physiology, ecology, and our evocative relationship with them. More on Michael and his book, *Bark: A Field Guide to Trees of the Northeast*, can be found at www.knowyourtrees.com.

CHUCK WOOSTER owns and runs Sunrise Farm in White River Junction, Vermont, producing meats, vegetables, maple syrup, and wood products. He's a board member of the Upper Valley Land Trust and a regular contributor to the *Valley News*, a daily paper in Lebanon, New Hampshire.

# INDEX

# INDEX

## About the New Hampshire Charitable Foundation

The New Hampshire Charitable Foundation is New Hampshire's statewide community foundation, founded in 1962 by and for the people of New Hampshire. We manage a growing collection of more than 1,700 funds created by generous individuals, families and businesses, and award more than $30 million in grants and scholarships every year. We work with generous and visionary citizens to maximize the power of their giving, support great work happening in our communities and lead and collaborate on high-impact initiatives. Learn more at **www.nhcf.org**.

NEW HAMPSHIRE
CHARITABLE FOUNDATION

## About Northern Woodlands

The Center for Northern Woodlands ("Northern Woodlands"), a non-profit organization, works to increase understanding of and appreciation for the natural wonders, economic productivity and ecological integrity of the region's forests. It publishes *The Outside Story* weekly ecology series, *Northern Woodlands* magazine, and other publications focused on forest stewardship. To learn more, including how schools can sign up for free digital magazine subscriptions, see **www.northernwoodlands.org**.

Northern
Woodlands